The Relevance of Teilhard

THE RELEVANCE OF TEILHARD

R. Wayne Kraft

FIDES PUBLISHERS, INC.
Notre Dame, Indiana

Library of Congress Catalog Card Number: 68-57408

DEDICATION

To my wife, Joan, who helped me immeasurably in this undertaking in so many ways, and to my children, Steven, Brian, Kevin and Ellen for being so tolerant of their Dad during the writing of 'his Teilhard book.'

The age of nations is past. The task before us now, if we would not perish, is to shake off our ancient prejudices, and to build the earth. (i)

* * * * *

Fascism, Communism, democracy, have ceased to have any real meaning. My own dream would be to see the best of humanity regrouped on a spiritual basis determined by the following three aims: Universalism, Futurism and Personalism, and cooperating in whatever political and economic movement should prove technically most able to safeguard these three aims. (ii)

* * * * *

If we are to avoid total anarchy, the source and sign of universal death, we can do no other than plunge resolutely forward, even though something in us perish, into the melting-pot of socialization.

Though something in us perish?

But where is it written that he who loses his soul shall save it? (iii)

Pierre Teilhard de Chardin

PREFACE

Pierre Teilhard de Chardin was a Frenchman, a Jesuit priest and a world renowned paleontologist, who within a short twelve years after his death has been acclaimed by political leaders, scientists, scholars and religious leaders of many faiths throughout the world as one of the most remarkable men who ever lived. Like most other outstanding men known to history he has also been vilified and condemned by other members of the same groups. Whether right or wrong, clearly he *was* an outstanding man to have drawn such attention from so many people with diverse interests in such a short span of time.

His writings, the most significant of which were published posthumously, and are still being published by a literary executor, all focus to a greater or lesser extent on one central theme—evolution. For Fr. Teilhard evolution had a much broader connotation than it has for most of us. To him evolution was, in a sense, everything—the heavens, the earth, living organisms past, present, and future, man, society itself. It was a dimension, a process, an underlying phenomenon common to everything that ever was or ever will be. Evolution provided Fr. Teilhard with the key to understanding life, which often-times appears absurd and meaningless, in this 20th century world; simultaneously it strengthened his faith in God, his faith in Christ and his faith in the Church.

Although the literary style of his prose is eloquent to the point of being poetic at times, many of the details of his 'theory of evolution' are complex. This fact combined with the sheer volume of his writings and the additional fact that most of his important works are a blend of science, philosophy and theology have caused many people to despair of understanding what Fr. Teilhard said. This book has been written for these people. It is an attempt, by a layman who is not a paleontologist, philosopher, or theologian, to summarize Fr. Teilhard's ideas on evolution for laymen who are not paleontologists, philosophers, or theologians.

The reader, especially if he is totally unfamiliar with the vast scope of Fr. Teilhard's concepts, may be saying to himself "This sounds fine for those who like that sort of thing but I'm not really interested in evolution. Evoluntionary theory is irrelevant to me, to my problems of earning a living in this hectic, crisis-ridden 20th century." In response to this type of reaction, I would like to say at the outset, that Fr. Teilhard's writings *are* relevant, terrifyingly relevant today . . . to all of us.

In fact my primary purpose in writing this book is to help people find "the world of Teilhard." I believe that if more of us would "know" Teilhard and understand more fully what he is trying to tell us, we would all be more strongly motivated to act according to our understanding. This modern world then would inevitably be a much better place in which to live.

Fr. Teilhard was an optimist but not a shallow or superficial optimist. He believed man would eventually build a better world but he also recognized that this would only come about through mankind working together and with the evolutionary tide—not against it. He devoted his life to combating pessimism, defeatism, nihilism and all the other negative philosophies which tend to lead men to work and war against one another and against the evolutionary forces, which, he believed, were an inherent and inescapable part of our universe. He saw a supremely glorious way out of the maze of seemingly overwhelming problems facing mankind today—the problems of a potential nuclear holocaust, of an imminent population and/or pollution explosion, of preserving human values in a technological-computerized-socialized society.

The beauty of his solution to these problems and countless others like them is that it is so simple. But really it's not Fr. Teilhard's solution—it's Christ's. Fundamentally the solution to our problems which Fr. Teilhard tried to make us see is nothing more than the age-old message writ large in the Bible—love God and love your neighbor. He has translated, so to speak, the Bible message (i.e., salvation history) into an idiom which is meaningful to scientifically-pragmatically minded 20th century man. He has shown us, within an evolutionary framework, how to better understand our world, our society and ourselves. In so doing he has made it abundantly clear that we human beings have it within our power to save or destroy the world and ourselves—because we humans are "evolution become aware of itself." What Fr. Teilhard has given us is a very practical and urgently important reason (if we need one—and most of us do) for living Christ's message in *our every action* rather than merely giving lip service to it as we are prone to do.

It should be obvious that it is impossible to encompass all the ramifications of Fr. Teilhard's lifework in one short volume; this book, therefore, should only be considered as an introduction to his ideas. It is my hope that it will serve this purpose of introduction and give the reader sufficient knowledge of the general features of Fr. Teilhard's vision so that he can more easily find his way among the original works and the numerous more scholarly commentaries which are appearing in ever greater numbers on the bookshelves of the world.

Finally I would like to acknowledge with sincere thanks the several friends who have graciously given of their time to help me write this book. Mrs. Vernon J. Kraft of Oconomowoc, Wisconsin and Rev. James P. Finnegan, OSFS, Chairman of The Division of Philosophy and Theology at Allentown College, Center Valley, Pennsylvania reviewed the entire typescript and made many constructive criticisms. For the most part their suggestions have been incorporated into the text. To Professors James E. Sturm and Francis A. Trembley, of the chemistry and biology departments respectively of Lehigh University I am especially indebted. Their stimulating discussions and critical reviews of those portions of the draft relevant to their fields of competence were invaluable to me.

By acknowledging this assistance I do not mean to shift the blame for any shortcomings this book possesses. It was written by me and represents my interpretation of Fr. Teilhard's thought. Therefore, let me add, I am fully aware that my interpretation is most certainly indebted to and colored by my particular experiences, education, conversations I've had with diverse people, books and reviews I have read—in short, it is a product of my milieu and not that of anyone else.

R. Wayne Kraft
Bethlehem, Pa.

CONTENTS

THE MAN

Ideas, like everything else in this world, do not suddenly appear 'out of the blue,' completely articulated and finally formed. They evolve. As we shall see in this book it is virtually impossible to trace anything, including an idea or a theory, back to its origin. It is only when ideas or theories or animals or men or political systems have evolved to a point that they are significantly different from that from which they evolved that we can recognize them as new. Nevertheless there does come a time when a new idea or organism or whatever-it-is is recognized as such. In this sense Fr. Pierre Teilhard de Chardin's theory of evolution also evolved. Not only did he build upon the work of men who had gone before him, Linnaeus, Lamarck and Darwin to name just a few, but his theory also evolved in his own mind throughout the course of his life.

His fame has arisen because he was the first man to clearly express what we might call a recognizably new theory of evolution. But if it were only this, if it were just a new theory of evolution, it probably would never have received the attention, nor he the renown, which it and he have. However, his theory is much more than merely a new theory; it is also a rule of action, a religion and a presentment. To a greater or lesser extent it encompasses all of man's knowledge of the universe as obtained over the course of the centuries from both science (physical, natural and social) and Revelation. Since it is so all inclusive and inspiring to so many people (although there are others to whom it is "mythology," "height of confusion," "poison") Fr. Teilhard has rightly, in my opinion, been called a prophet of our times.

It is not the purpose of this book to try to follow, as far back as we can, the origin of the ideas for which Fr. Teilhard is known. However it is considered to be worthwhile to devote a few pages to a thumbnail biographical sketch of the "originator" of this new theory of evolution so that the reader will have a deeper appreciation of the character of the scientist who, towards the end of his life, wrote the following lines—

> Jesus-Omega, grant me to *serve you*, to proclaim you, to glorify you, to make you manifest, to the very end through all the time that remains to me in life, and above all through my death. Desperately, Lord Jesus, I commit to your care my last active years, and my death: do not let them impair or spoil the work I have dreamed of achieving for you.[1]

* * * * * *

Pierre, the fourth of eleven children, was born to Marie and Joseph Teilhard de Chardin on May 1, 1881 at the family home of Sarcenat in the Auvergne district of central France. Until their deaths his relationships with his parents were of the warmest kind as his letters to them testify. From his father, a learned gentleman farmer, he acquired at an early age an appreciation for natural things and from his mother, a cultured woman and devout Catholic, he received what he called, upon hearing of her death many years later, 'the best part of my soul.' It was she who gave him his immense capacity for love, compassion and understanding and his lifelong devotion to his church, even though in later years it sorely tried him. At the age of eleven, as was customary among well-to-do French families of that time, he was enrolled in a Jesuit 'college' at Villefranche on the Rhone. He did well in school in all subjects other than religion, not because God did not interest him but, apparently, because of the way in which the material in the courses was presented.

During his late adolescent years Pierre decided to become a Jesuit priest and accordingly entered the seminary at Aix-en-Provence for his novitiate in 1899. Three years later the seminary was forced to move to the island of Jersey off the west coast of Normandy because of a wave of anticlericalism in France. It was here that his life-long interest in geology and paleontology became fixed; the island, rich in fossil-bearing rocks, provided him ample opportunity for field work and study in these scientific specialties.

At the completion of his philosophy, classics and natural science studies at Jersey in 1905, Pierre Teilhard was assigned to teach chemistry and physics in one of the Jesuit schools in Cairo. His spare time while in Egypt was devoted to exploring the deserts in the vicinity for paleontological specimens. The results of some of these expeditions formed the subject matter of his first scientific papers. Following this three year maturing period characteristic of Jesuit training, Pierre entered upon his theological studies at Hastings in England. He was ordained a priest three years later, in 1911, and completed his formal priestly training after one more year of theology at the same school.

Having decided upon a secular career in the fields of geology and paleontology and wishing to advance his knowledge in these areas he seized an opportunity to study with the great Marcellin Boule and the Abbé Henri Breuil and therefore returned to Paris in 1912. In addition to laboratory work classifying fossils under these men in the Paris museum of natural history he participated in 'digs' throughout northern Europe with international teams of paleontologists. One of these expeditions, back to Hastings, involved him in what subsequently proved to be the famous Piltdown Man Hoax. Upon learning of the solution to this paradoxical paleontological problem forty years later Fr. Teilhard wrote the following note to Dr. K. P. Oakley of the British Museum who had helped solve it.

> I congratulate you most sincerely on your solution of the Piltdown problem. Anatomically speaking, 'Eoanthropus' was a kind of monster. And, from a paleontological point of view, it was equally shocking that a 'dawn-Man' could occur in England. Therefore I am fundamentally pleased by your conclusions, in spite of the fact that, sentimentally speaking, it spoilt one of my brightest and earliest paleontological memories.[2]

World War I broke not long after Fr. Teilhard became thoroughly involved in this work and he was soon drafted into the French army as a priest stretcher-bearer. During the next three years (1914–17) he saw service in some of the bitterest fighting of the war. The experience had a lasting effect on him—it deepened his feeling of compassion for his fellow-men, his love for God, and his sense of the spirit-of-earth. Because he preferred to share the sufferings of the troops in the trenches and to help whenever and however he could, he refused promotion to officer rank as Chaplain. At the conclusion of the war his heroism had won him the Croix de Guerre, the Médaille Militaire and the Chevalier du Légion d'Honneur.

His experiences in battle and the deepening insights which he developed during this trying period increased his resolve to devote the balance of his life towards reconciling matter and spirit by the concept which was already becoming clear in his mind. A passage, one of many similar ones, from a letter written to his cousin near the end of the war poignantly expresses this dedication.

> I can see, in sudden, clear, vivid, impressions, that my strength and my joy derive from seeing in some way made real for me the fusion of God and the world, the latter giving *'immediacy'* to the divine, and the divine spiritualizing the tangible.[3]

However, he recognized that he needed more technical training and, so, upon demobilization in 1919, he entered the Sorbonne to begin work on a doctorate in natural sciences. His thesis work on the mammals of the Lower Eocene Period in France won prizes from the Academy of Sciences and the Geological Society of France and resulted in two more scientific papers. Thus in 1922 at the age of forty and already a recognized authority in his field, he was appointed lecturer in geology at the Catholic Institute.

The next year Fr. Teilhard received an invitation to spend what proved to be the first of many years in China. He accepted the opportunity and obtained permission from his superiors to participate. With Fr. Licent, a fellow Jesuit, the first expedition was to the Ordos desert where they discovered traces of Paleolithic man in China. After the trip, back in Paris, Fr. Teilhard published a large number of scientific papers based on the observations he had made in China.

Throughout the period since World War II and simultaneously with his scientific work Fr. Teilhard had been engaging in priestly duties. In addition he had been writing extensively on the religious implications of his work. Most of the essays never saw print until after his death because many of his ideas were considered too unorthodox by various authorities in the Church. Nevertheless his influence among friends and students increased markedly; his lectures, essays and spiritual works were copied and appealed widely to the young intellectuals with whom he came in contact. His outspokenness on many traditionally expressed doctrines of the Church, such as original sin, sincerely disturbed his superiors and so, in 1925, he received instructions, 'sympathetically given,' to concentrate on scientific work and return to China.

It is important in understanding the character of Fr. Teilhard to recognize that he obediently accepted this 'banishment,' as he did all the other disappointments in his life, with a complete lack of rebelliousness. Throughout his seventy-four years he lived as he preached and prayed—

> that the Spirit may always shine forth in me, that I may not succumb to the temptation that lies in wait for every act of boldness, nor ever forget that *you alone* must be sought in and through everything, you, Lord, will send me—at what moments only you know—deprivations, disappointments, sorrow. What is to be brought about is more than a simple union: it is a *transformation,* in the course of which the only thing

> our human activity can do is humbly, to make ourselves ready, and to accept.[4]

It is not considered necessary to chronicle all of Fr. Teilhard's travels in the period 1925–1945. Sufficient to say that his headquarters were at Peking, that he traveled extensively in China, India and the far east on paleontological expeditions, visited America several times attending scientific conferences and giving lectures and returned to France occasionally for brief visits. It was during this period that he became known, among his other scientific accomplishments, for his work as one of the codiscoverers of the so-called Peking Man, one of our ancient forebears who lived about 400,000 years ago. During this period he published numerous scientific papers, wrote many other spiritual essays which he sent to friends, and became advisor to the Chinese Geological Service. The Japanese control over China during World War II severely restricted his travels but provided him an opportunity to do a lot of museum work and to write what he and many other people consider to be his most significant book, *The Phenomenon of Man.* Another major disappointment in his life, accepted like the others without embitterment, was that he was not permitted by Church authority to have this book published during his lifetime. With Jesuit approval it and his other not-strictly-scientific works were willed to a literary executor to be published after his death.

After the second World War he returned to his homeland as a respected scholar and priest. For the next five years he engaged in scientific and philosophical-theological conferences and discussions, wrote several of his major works (*Man's Place in Nature, The Vision of the Past*), traveled to South Africa to inspect first-hand the major new paleontological discoveries being made there —and suffered a heart attack which permanently impaired his physical stamina. The Church however still considered his ideas dangerous with the result that the optimistic spirit, characteristic of all his writings, was almost—but not quite—broken when his Jesuit superiors did not allow him to accept the highest academic chair the French could offer in his field. And so in 1951 he was again requested to leave France. No longer able to engage in rigorous field work, he joined the staff of the Wenner-Gren Foundation in New York City as a Research Fellow. There he continued his writing and drew up plans for organized research to be conducted by the foundation. One more trip to Africa in 1953 completed his world travels.

Fr. Teilhard died on Easter Sunday (the day on which he had hoped to die) in 1955, with friends, after attending Mass at St. Patrick's Cathedral in New York City.

* * * * * *

Any book about Fr. Teilhard would be grossly inadequate if it did not say something about his works. For the benefit of the reader, whom I assume will be American without a reading knowledge of French, I have listed below the titles of each of his books which have so far been translated into English. A brief critique of each is also given to enable the reader to select those books which most interest him.

The Phenomenon of Man, published by Harper and Row, is Fr. Teilhard's most famous, and first published book. When it first appeared in France shortly after his death in 1955 it was the bestselling non-fiction book of the year. It contains a sympathetic introduction written by Sir Julian Huxley, Fr. Teilhard's friend even though the two men did not see eye-to-eye on the philosophical-religious implications of The Phenomenon. The book is Fr. Teilhard's most comprehensive treatment of his theory. It consists of twelve chapters divided into four books entitled Before Life Came, Life, Thought and Survival. An Epilogue entitled The Christian Phenomenon and a Postscript and an Appendix complete the book. Many people apparently find this book difficult to understand—particularly if it is their first exposure to his writing—since it is quite detailed and, in some places rather technical. However any person who wants to learn more about Fr. Teilhard's ideas will certainly, sooner or later, want to read this book. It is the book of which Arnold Toynbee wrote—"A great man of science and a great soul. His work gives our generation the comprehensive view it sorely needs."

The Divine Milieu, published by Harper and Row, has been called by Karl Stern "one of the great spiritual testimonies of our time." Written in China during the winter of 1926–27 it was not published until 1957 in France and 1960 in the United States. It is an ascetic work written by Fr. Teilhard, the mystic, not Fr. Teilhard, the scientist. In his words

> (it) is not specifically addressed to Christians who are firmly established in their faith and have nothing more to learn about its beliefs. It is written for the waverers, both inside and outside; that is to say for those who, instead of giving themselves wholly to the Church, either hesitate on its threshold or turn away in the hope of surpassing it.[5]

It discusses what Fr. Teilhard calls man's activities and his passivities—what he does and what he undergoes—and explains how the individual can use his free will and his spiritual life to cooperate with God and go beyond what seems to be a purely material evolutionary process.

The Future of Man, published by Harper and Row, is a collection of twenty-three essays written between 1920 and 1953. Each is complete in itself. They have been arranged by the editors into their chronological order. Each essay treats a different aspect of Fr. Teilhard's common theme. There are essays on progress, education, research, the atom bomb, peace, the rights of man, democracy, the end of the world and, of course, some on the biological and paleontological aspects of evolution. Because each chapter is complete in itself and since there are a variety of approaches I usually recommend this book as one of the first which should be read by a person who is initiating his study of Fr. Teilhard.

Hymn of The Universe, published by Harper and Row, contains three major essays and a number of short pensees (thoughts) on a variety of topics selected from other works. The first essay, entitled "The Mass on The World," was written when Fr. Teilhard, on a scientific expedition in the Gobi Desert, found he had neither bread nor wine with which to celebrate the Mass, and was so moved to fulfill his priestly obligation that he submitted to God a substitute offering of the whole world. The second, "Christ in the World of Matter," consists of three short stories written about his innermost feelings but in the guise of a friend because they reveal such intimate details of his character. The last—"The Spiritual Power of Matter"—expresses, as the title indicates, an essential feature of his vision for he believed that nothing of the reality of the world, properly seen, was profane. It is perhaps significant to note that the latter two essays were written while he was still a corporal in the French army. The book, taken as a whole, tells us much about Fr. Teilhard's spiritual life and illumines the ideas behind his philosophy.

The Appearance of Man, published by Harper and Row, is another collection of essays, the most technical collection yet published in English in book form. For the serious student of paleontology it provides detailed explanations, diagrams and a few sketches of the remains of various precursors of Homo Sapiens. The book is broadly divided into five sections; the state of the problem at the turn of the century, the paleontological discoveries, the question of the "missing link," the phenomenon of "imbrication," and the peculiarities of the human species. The nonspecialist will find the book fascinating, if he can skim over the unfamiliar terms, because all of Fr. Teilhard's writings were meant to be understood—in contradistinction to much scientific writing today—and because each article usually contains a gem of a thought germane to his vision. A preface by Robert Francoeur helps put the volume in perspective and describes the major developments in paleontology in the ten years since Fr. Teilhard's death (i.e., Dr. L. S. B. Leakey's work at the Olduvai gorge in Tanzania).

Building the Earth, published by Dimension Books, consists of five rather short essays. In contrast to those in *The Appearance of Man*, which emphasize the past, these are concerned with the future and what Fr. Teilhard thought we, mankind, must do if we're going to save the world (viz., build the earth). His tremendous optimism and profound faith in the future and in the God of evolution shines forth particularly brightly in these essays.

Man's Place in Nature, published by Harper and Row, could rightfully be called a condensed version of *The Phenomenon of Man.* Being considerably shorter it is not as detailed as The Phenomenon. It was written several years after *The Phenomenon of Man* and suffered the same fate. Since Fr. Teilhard's ideas and mode of expression continued to develop until his death, this book is a valuable supplement to The Phenomenon and might be preferred by readers who don't wish to tackle his major work without more preparation.

Vision of The Past, published by Harper and Row, the most recently published collection of essays in English, might more properly be entitled Vision *from* the Past, because the essays as a group emphasize his vision *of* the future obtained *from* a study of the past (viz., paleontology). A considerable number of the essays were written to make absolutely clear his ideas on transformism—the change from one species to another through evolution. The chapters on man, his place in the evolutionary scheme of things, in nature and in the universe contain some of his most eloquent passages in which he tried to show that men are not dupes in some vast and pointless cosmological process, that life is not a blind alley but a road leading to a glorious future.

Letters From Egypt, 1905–1908 and *Letters from Paris, 1912–1914,* both published by Herder and Herder. The earlier letters in these two collections are typical of those many an articulate young man would write to his parents of his daily experiences. In the later letters one can see emerging that 'passion for the universe' which more definitely marked his later writings. These books will be of value to those interested in studying the earliest evolution of Fr. Teilhard's ideas in his own mind.

The Making of A Mind, published by Harper and Row, consists of the letters Fr. Teilhard wrote, primarily to his cousin, Marguerite Teillard-Chambon, during lulls in the battles of World War I. In her introduction to the book, Mlle. Chambon wrote that "of the outside events in Pierre Teilhard's life the war was probably most decisive of all. It had a profound effect on his whole being." Many of the letters consist of Fr. Teilhard's spiritual counsel to Marguerite. Others describe his own development and the emergence of his great vision of the human situation. Finally, there is an extraordinary detailed account of his day-to-day experiences at the front—his "baptism into reality." *The Making of A Mind* provides an indispensable understanding of the evolution of Fr. Teilhard's evolutionary theory.

Letters From A Traveler, published by Harper and Row, as the name implies, contains many of the letters Fr. Teilhard wrote to his relatives, friends, fellow priests and scientific associates throughout the world during the many years of his 'exile' from France. Maurice Dolbier of the New York Herald Tribune aptly expressed the value of this collection in a book review when he wrote: "These letters reveal the patience and courage with which Pierre Teilhard de Chardin did his work on this earth, and the passionate fervor with which he dedicated that work to the glory of God." Since, in many of the letters, he expressed new thoughts for the first time to his correspondents and reacted to their reactions this book provides an invaluable supplement to the collections of earlier letters and *The Making of A Mind* for those interested in following the development of his ideas.

Pierre Teilhard de Chardin–Maurice Blondel Correspondence, was edited by Henri de Lubac, translated by William Whitman and published by Herder and Herder. Fr. Maurice Blondel, Fr. Teilhard's senior by several years and a philosopher rather than a scientist, had a very significant influence upon the development of the younger man's thought, particularly its theological aspects. Of this meeting of two contemporary seminal minds it has been said: "Together Blondel and Teilhard created the atmosphere that made Vatican II possible." The letters themselves, written during the course of one month in 1919 and exchanged via a mutual friend, occupy only thirty pages in the book; the balance consists of extensive explanatory notes and commentary by the editor and a moving eulogy delivered by Fr. André Ravier on the tenth anniversary of Fr. Teilhard's death.

* * * * * *

To conclude this chapter on the man Pierre Teilhard de Chardin something should be said about his influence on the world after his death. The only word for it is fantastic. Innumerable articles have been written about him and his ideas in secular and religious magazines and newspapers throughout the world. Lectures and conferences too numerous to count on the scientific, philosophical and religious aspects of his vision have been held. Teilhard associations have been formed in many countries throughout the world.

Religious leaders of many faiths have praised his fundamental, albeit indirect, contributions to ecumenism. Pope Paul VI, for example, said that "Fr. Teilhard is an indispensable man for our times; his expression of faith is necessary for us."

Since Fr. Teilhard has been a controversial figure, especially within his church, it is in order to give further details relative to his standing vis a vis the Roman Catholic Church. As mentioned previously he was not allowed to publish his most significant works during his lifetime and, in fact, they have never been published with a *Nihil Obstat* and *Imprimatur* (official declarations that the books are free of doctrinal or moral error). About six months before the opening session of Vatican II, in March 1962, the Holy Office exercised its traditional watchdog policy and issued a *monitum* (warning) against "ambiguities and even grave errors" in his writings. Pope John XXIII did not sign the *monitum* and is reported to have said later that the incident was "regrettable." (It is interesting to note that in 1963 Pope John adopted some expressions traceable to Fr. Teilhard in his widely acclaimed encyclical *Pacem in Terris.*)

Later, at the Council, Cardinal Koenig in speaking for 'aggiornamento' said "Teilhard went further than anyone else in dedicating himself to the task of finding positive evidence of agreement between science and religion. Would it not be worthwhile for groups to follow up his basic ideas?" Fr. Teilhard was often quoted on the floor of the Council and in the opinion of more than one writer had an influence on the outcome of that historic council comparable to that of Pope John XXIII. For example, Fr. D. R. Campion, who prepared the commentary and explanatory notes for the English language edition of the *Pastoral Con-*

stitution on the Church in the Modern World, Vatican II's most important document, wrote "Here, as elsewhere, it is easy to recognize the compatibility of insights developed by thinkers such as Teilhard de Chardin in his *Divine Milieu* with the fundamental outlook of the Council."

There have been other developments since then e.g., Pope Paul's discourse with theologians in July 1966 on original sin, but nothing else to my knowledge which adds substantially to the picture just painted. All things considered, it appears to me, a Catholic layman, that the Church is taking a middle of the road policy and that it is proceeding cautiously, as it must, in adapting 'the Teilhardian spirit' to its wordly mission.

Reaction outside the Church has also been mixed although the overall impression one gets is that his defenders far outnumber his detractors. Although he has received that special opposition reserved for original thinkers from a few scientists and writers he has also been quoted in a favorable context by scientists from many disciplines and by political leaders and philosophers from many lands. In 1965 he was honored, with Albert Einstien, by UNESCO. These two geniuses, as Mr. Rene Maheu put it, who died within eight days of one another and within a few miles of one another will perhaps give future historians reason to pause and reflect on this striking coincidence; and comparing these two destinies, these two achievements, these two quests, these two certitudes—so profoundly different—they will perhaps see one of the signs most representative of our complex age.

As several commentators have pointed out Fr. Teilhard was only human and his theory contains flaws. Depending on one's point of view they completely negate his whole concept or, at the other extreme, are merely relatively minor defects which those who come after him must correct. Judging from the several authoritative books which have been written about Fr. Teilhard it would appear that most competent observers and scholars believe that his fundamental concept is substantially correct and compatible with the world as we know it. By 'compatible with the world as we know it' is meant compatible with our scientific knowledge of the universe and the world, with history, with the social milieu in which we live, with modern Bible exegesis, and with the fundamental teachings of Christianity, particularly Catholicism.

Since the reader of this book may be interested in these evaluations I have given below a synopsis of several of the more comprehensive ones which have been published in English.

- *Teilhard de Chardin, Scientist and Seer*, by Canon Charles E. Raven, Harper and Row. The author, a member of the Anglican faith, was, before his retirement, Regius Professor of Divinity at Cambridge University and master of Christ Church College, Cambridge. Canon Raven places great emphasis on the influences which shaped Fr. Teilhard's thought; his book therefore is an excellent biography. But it is more than that for he focuses attention, in separate chapters, on each of several aspects of Fr. Teilhard's vision. Canon Raven is obviously well read and thoroughly familiar with his subject's work and thought. Although he never knew Fr. Teilhard and is not a scientist, he has produced a book which is one of the most comprehensive—and sympathetic—evaluations yet published.
- *Teilhard de Chardin—The Man and His Meaning*, by Fr. Henri de Lubac, S.J., Hawthorn Books,

Inc. This book, in contrast to Canon Raven's, does not devote as much space to the historical-biographical aspects of Fr. Teilhard's writings. Nor is it as comprehensive in its coverage. Rather it emphasizes and defends Fr. Teilhard's Christianity. Since Fr. Teilhard lived and worked for much of his life among scientists and pragmatists who could not or would not see that their view of the world was but the other side of the coin from a religious view his expression of Christianity has an apologetic nature. In the first two thirds of this book Fr. de Lubac has skillfully drawn and analyzed a picture of Fr. Teilhard's view of his religion. In the last third he has defined the essentially catechetical purpose to which Fr. Teilhard devoted his life, explained his approaches and methods, and shown how they influenced his writing. Fr. de Lubac effectively deals with Fr. Teilhard's most outspoken critics yet at the same time he is eminently fair and points out some of the weak points in his theory.

- *Teilhard de Chardin and The Mystery of Christ*, by Fr. Christopher F. Mooney, S.J., Harper and Row. The scope of this book, by an American priest, roughly parallels Fr. de Lubac's. In a sense its content is even more restricted because Fr. Mooney's book focuses almost entirely on Fr. Teilhard's Christology. Some of the other aspects of Catholic belief or practices which Fr. de Lubac discusses in more detail, viz. the Virgin Mary, are only mentioned briefly in passing. The prime value of this absorbing study is that it is more than an examination of Fr. Teilhard's thought: it is an extension thereof. Building upon Fr. Teilhard's key concepts Fr. Mooney, a theologian (which Fr. Teilhard wasn't), has presented a reconstruction and interpretation of the Christological thought of Fr. Teilhard. If there is one key idea to this synthesis it is that one cannot hope to understand Christ—and the world—

within a static framework because change is a fact of life. For the believer and unbeliever alike Fr. Mooney has shown how, within Fr. Teilhard's dynamic evolutionary framework, "the most traditional Christianity, expressed in Baptism, The Cross and The Eucharist, can be interpreted so as to embrace all that is best in the aspirations which are characteristic of our age."

- *Teilhard and The Creation of The Soul,* by Fr. Robert North, S.J., Bruce Publishing Company. One of the criticisms that has been leveled against Fr. Teilhard is that 'he didn't know what to do with original sin.' Fr. North has jumped right into the middle of this question, so to speak. From numerous sources—the Bible, various official pronouncements and documents from the Roman Catholic Church, Fr. Teilhard's writings and those of other scholars—he has collected all pertinent material and then thoroughly and systematically analyzed it with a legal-like precision. He concludes that the exact mode of creation of the soul is an open theological question, as is the (scientific) question of monogenism vs. polygenism. This book, one of a series of theology textbooks, is extensively documented. A valuable feature is the one page summary at the end of each chapter. Fr. Karl Rahner provided the introduction to this scholarly treatise and concluded with the following:

> The present volume merits praise and interest not only because it brings an important open question of theology clearly to the forefront of attention and debate. It gathers together also an extraordinary abundance of materials out of the most varied theological disciplines relevant to the solution of its question. This will make it easier for every theologically-minded reader to form his own independent judgment.

Another work appropriate to this section and one of several recently published books on the subject of original sin is Fr. A. Hulsbosch's *God in Creation and Evolution* published by Sheed and Ward. Although Fr.Teilhard's name is scarcely mentioned and he is never quoted, the book is dedicated to him with the following words:

> Although Teilhard was no professional theologian, he nevertheless did what the theologians had not done: he was the first after the rise of the natural sciences to speak about God and Christ in terms of the scientific image. That is his immortal merit, which has perhaps not yet been sufficiently admitted. I should consider it a great honor were these pages regarded as a tribute to the memory of this pioneer who on Easter 1955, went to the vision of his Creator.

Fr. Hulsbosch's theme and conclusions are practically identical to those of Fr. North. His book however differs from the former in that it is not a treatise on the work of Fr. Teilhard. Instead it is a strictly original work drawing exclusively upon the Bible in an attempt at a new formulation of the teaching of the Church about original sin.

None of the books about Fr. Teilhard mentioned so far can be considered as a comprehensive biography. However an excellent one has been written by Dr. Claude Cuenot, a friend of his subject. It includes an exhaustive list of Fr. Teilhard's writings (over 500 entries) and has been translated into English by Vincent Colimere. It bears the title *Pierre Teilhard de Chardin* and is published by Helicon Press. Also availiable is the *Teilhard de Chardin Album*, by Jeanne Mortier and Marie-Louise Auboux. Selected quotations accompany the photographs in this beautifully illustrated pictorial biography published by Harper and Row.

HIS VISION

Three days before he died Fr. Teilhard made the cogent notation in his journal which is quoted below. This entry, which proved to be his last, summarizes in remarkably few words the vision or theory or concept to which he devoted his life. Each of the three parts is important; all are interrelated and none can be neglected. Because it is such a condensed summary using words coined* by Fr. Teilhard and referring to a passage of Scripture whose meaning is not obvious the chances are that many of the ramifications of what is implied are not clear to those unfamiliar with his work. The purpose of this chapter therefore is to describe some of the principle features of his vision. Through this a deeper meaning may become apparent and the essential unity of his ideas may be brought into sharper focus.

Here is his final summary.

What I believe. . . Maundy Thursday, 7 April 1955

1. St. Paul–the three verses: *En pasi panti Theos.* (God all in all.)

[The three verses are 1 Cor 15:26–28:

And the last enemy to be destroyed will be death,
for "he has put all things under his feet."
But when he says all things are subject to him,

* New words coined by Fr. Teilhard and other technical terms are briefly defined in the glossary but are more fully explained when they are discussed in their place in the book.

undoubtedly he is excepted who has subjected all things to him.
And when all things are made subject to him, then the Son himself will also be made subject to him who subjected all things to him, that God may be all in all.

2. Cosmos = Cosmogenesis-Biogenesis-Noogenesis-Christogenesis.
3. The two articles of my Credo
   a–The Universe is centrated–Evolutively-
      Upward
      Forward
   b–Christ in its Centre–The Christian Phenomenon
      Noogenesis=Christogenesis(=Paul)[6]

Before delving into the details and trying to describe Fr. Teilhard's ideas as I think he meant us to understand them a few comments of a general nature are necessary. To fully appreciate his thought it is important to realize that his theory or vision or whatever one chooses to call it is more than a theory of evolution because it is also a religion, a rule for action, and a presentiment. Thus there are four interrelated aspects to it:

a) It is a theory in the sense that it is a description of our universe which incorporates, to varying degrees, all our knowledge of the universe as deduced from the physical sciences, the natural sciences and the social sciences within one dynamic evolutionary system.
b) It is a religious outlook which is Christian to its core. The power of his writing and the example of his life illustrate how intimately the teachings of Christ are related to a world in evolution. Furthermore Fr. Teilhard's concept enables one to see how

all the major religions of the world may and perhaps will, in time, converge through evolution.

c) It is a rule for action because it shows us how to resolve the *apparent* dichotomies between science and religion, between humanism and Christianity and between different religions. He has shown us that there is no real conflict between man's desire for personal freedom and the world-wide and inescapable tendency towards socialization *or* between man's need to earn his bread by the sweat of his brow and his desire for a better life on earth and/or in heaven. All that needs to be seen is that any of these supposed conflicts-of-interest can be resolved by each of us living the rule of action which Christ preached.

d) Lastly his concept of reality is a presentiment in the sense that he has predicted, in a logical fashion it seems to me, the structure or character which our world-wide human society will probably tend to assume in the future, (i.e., the direction in which society will move). Furthermore Fr. Teilhard's vision gives us a dazzling picture of what our end and the end of the world may be like.

Unquestionably Fr. Teilhard was able to look at the results of science, the nature of society and the essential meaning of various religions, particularly Christianity, in a light and within a framework which others had not been able to do previously. As Loren Eiseley, Provost of the University of Pennsylvania and an eminent evolutionist, said he had "a soaring mind which was capable of reading, in the stony hieroglyphs of nature, a spiritual message denied to a lesser man."

* * * * * *

A principle central to Fr. Teilhard's vision which will provide a convenient starting point for this exposition is expressible in the following manner: *Evolution is an irreversible process, not yet completed, which from the beginning has always proceeded in one discernible direction.* This principle enabled him to recognize an essential unity to *everything* in the universe. Seen in the light in which he saw them, all natural phenomena and the phenomenon of man (with all *that* implies) confirmed his belief that this principle was valid and that his vision of reality was a true vision.

Evolution is a process. This key idea is implied by item two in his summary, which states that the cosmos is describable by four words, each of which has the suffix 'genesis.' According to the dictionary genesis means the coming into being of anything and cosmos means the universe conceived as an orderly and harmonious system. What Fr. Teilhard was trying to express in capsule form by item two in his formula therefore is that everything, by which he meant every thing and every non-thing—that is, the universe—is part of an orderly process coming into being. That is to say, at the root of his vision is the idea—the belief—that the world, in fact the whole universe, is not a static reality subject only to random pointless fluctuations in the arrangement of the matter of which it is composed. Rather, the universe is a dynamic reality which always was, is now, and always will be in the process of evolving in a certain general direction.

He believed that there is a recognizable pattern beneath the random motions of atoms in matter long noted by physicists, in the growth of living organisms observed by paleontologists and biologists and in the activities of men as recorded by history. By its use of the four words cosmogenesis, biogenesis, noogenesis and Christogenesis Fr. Teilhard's formula expresses the thought that the underlying process is recognizable. The sequence of the words expresses the additional idea of irreversibility, the thought that there *is* a discernible direction to all evolution. Stated another way, he believed that the heavens, the solar system, our earth, all living things, we people, man-made things of all kinds, social institutions of all types, even Christ, are not static. They, we and He are integral parts of a vast dynamic cosmological process coming into being. In other words the cosmos is a process and somehow God is related to it.

In order to describe this universal trend which he saw Fr. Teilhard introduced the terms 'without' and 'within.' They are words describing two different aspects of 'things' of the world.

The Without and the Within

By the without of things Fr. Teilhard means the physical reality of objects or beings. It is the tangible part of things, creatures and institutions. It is that which we can see, weigh, measure, manipulate in scientific experiments and transforms from one form to another by technology. When we speak of atoms, minerals, molecules and machines it is difficult for us to visualize that they have anything other than a without. After all, how could atoms of hydrogen, for example, have individual 'personalities,' unique characteristics which distinguish one from another? They rigorously obey the laws of probability and as far as we can determine experimentally belong strictly to the realm of physics.

Nevertheless Fr. Teilhard presents very logical arguments to support his view that everything, including an atom, has, in addition to its without, an inner nature of some kind. This he called the within. The within is intangible but nevertheless real. In the lower form of things, that is, in inert matter as opposed to living organisms, the within is not apparent to us because its intensity is so low. But as we move up the scale to higher forms of 'things' the within becomes more perceptible just as the radiation emitted by a piece of steel becomes more perceptible the hotter it becomes. For all practical purposes the within can be neglected by physicists and inorganic chemists when engaged in their professional work. Even a bacteriologist does not have to be unduly concerned with it. But a biologist has difficulty in explaining many natural phenomena solely from the physicochemical viewpoint. How for example, using only a knowledge of physics, chemistry and mechanics, does one explain how it is that a spider knows how to spin its web? The mechanistic attitude seems merely futile when we consider the vertebrates and "it breaks down completely with man, in whom the existence of a *within* can no longer be evaded, because it is the object of a direct intuition and the substance of all knowledge."[7]

The basic idea therefore is that the 'things' of the world can be arranged into some sort of more or less continuous series according to their degree of withinness. Near one end of the spectrum (i.e–in atoms) the without predominates and the within is so diffuse or weak that it can not be detected. As we move along the series the relative proportion, or more precisely, the relative importance, of the without and the within tends to shift. For example an automobile, which is basically a machine composed of inert matter, is nevertheless a reasonably complex arrangement of materials and it begins to show faint vestiges of 'personality.' At the least, each one of them is unique. If we place man along this scale he still has a without, a body, but he also has a within, a soul, which to a large extent governs his behavior.

Fr. Teilhard is not the only man to have conceived of this idea of some sort of prelife in so-called inert matter. It was Democritus, the Greek philosopher who died in 370BC, who first pointed out that since man is obviously something more than matter that 'something more' must have been present in some form or other in the matter from which man is made. In more recent times eminent biologists such as J. B. S Haldane and many others have expressed the same thought.

One other point should be made with respect to the scale we have been discussing on which 'things' can be placed according to the relative importance of the without and the within which they exhibit. It should be noted that we have not, yet, attempted to place an origin or a terminal point, a left end or a right end, a floor or a ceiling on the scale. All that we have tried to convey are Fr. Teilhard's thoughts that everything in the universe has two aspects to it, that the without and the within occur in different proportions in different 'things,' and that 'things' can, in principle, be rated or ranked along the scale according to the relative importance of the without and the within. But the question of what lies at either end of this scale, i.e., pure without or pure within, has been carefully avoided up to this point. (Since the question has been brought up it will have to be answered—but later.)

The without and the within are different features of the intrinsic nature of 'things.' While it is true that we can *sometimes* neglect the 'within' without introducing appreciable errors into our work, for example when performing physics experiments or transforming matter from one form to another to suit our practical purposes, Fr. Teilhard believed that it was essential to keep both components of 'things' in mind in order to understand evolution. This he did in formulating his "law" of evolution which we shall describe in the next section.

Evolutionary Law of Increasing Complexity

The principle of evolution which Fr. Teilhard believed was well documented by geology, paleontology, biology and history, is that more complex 'things' tend to survive and dominate other 'things' which are less complex. This notion is so far reaching and has so many implications that it must be developed in some detail. I will follow Fr. Teilhard's outline in *The Phenomenon of Man* and *Man's Place in Nature* to do this.

The simplest way to begin is obviously with a definition of complexity and with the simplest things . . . Complexity is defined in terms of the *number of elements* a 'thing' possesses *and* in terms of the *organization* among the elements. Both parts of the definition are important because it is not merely a question of size alone but organized or centrated-complexity which determines whether one 'thing' is more complex than another. Fr. Teilhard placed great emphasis on the two different parts of the definition of complexity just as he did on the dual aspect of 'things.' The quality or characteristic or property of complexity which a 'thing' possesses therefore depends; one, on the number of smaller entities of which the 'thing' is composed (e.g.—number of atoms in a molecule) *and*, two, on the number, type and quality of interdependent links between the separate elements comprising the 'thing' under consideration (e.g.—number, type and strength of chemical bonds in a molecule). "A fixed number of elements, a closed whole: this twofold characteristic of complexity must be emphasized, for on it depends the whole course of the thesis developed here." [8]

Thus an atom has more complexity than the nucleons of which it is constituted because an atom is more than aggregate of electrons, protons, neutrons, etc. It is a closed whole (containing a fixed number of elements) which has properties unique to itself. Similarly molecules rank above atoms. A molecule of water, for example, has entirely different properties than its constituent hydrogen and oxygen atoms. It also is a closed whole with a fixed number of interrelated parts, an organization of its own. A drop of water however is not more complex than a single molecule of water. Neither is a large crystal more complex than a small one. In each, the drop of water and the crystal, more atoms or molecules can be added or subtracted without changing the nature of the substance. The earth, the sun and stars, since they seem to possess no organization (or very little) and no centricity rank rather low on a centrated-complexity scale in spite of their size.

With this idea in mind we can now think of a centrated-complexity scale something like the following:

. . . nucleon <atom <molecule <virus < living cell . . .

Fr. Teilhard believed this scale characterizes in some way a dimension of our universe not hitherto recognized with sufficient clarity. He is not saying that complexity, per se, is a fifth dimension, one to be added to our one temporal and three spatial dimensions. Rather, increasing complexity is a measure of time and of life. It would be taking us too far astray to elaborate upon this point here but let us see what other ramifications he attached to the centrated-complexity scale.*

First of all he noted that this scheme is *natural* because it is based upon the intimate structure of things. The structure or physical configuration of a living cell is more complex than that of a virus, that of a virus more complex than that of a molecule, and so forth. A complexity scale therefore is

* The meaning of time and the meaning of life have always been an enigma to man. Superficially we think we know what the words mean but when we try to understand them more deeply we usually find ourselves in a sea of words and frequently end up by floundering around, like a ship on a stormy sea without an anchor, not really knowing what the words mean. Fr. Teilhard put it this way. He said that we are in the process of discovering time and the meaning of life as we learn more about our earth, its history and evolution, and about ourselves, where we came from and where we're going.

assuredly natural; it is a logical one to use in trying to understand the cosmos. More importantly, the scale is significant because it brings to light a relationship among all things in the universe. Allhough we can not yet define complexity in a manner which is applicable with equal rigour to all things, scientific evidence from many disciplines points to the fact that 'things' of the world, when arranged according to their complexity, also fall in line according to the *historical order of their birth*. That is to say, the elements along a complexity scale, generally speaking, succeed one another in time. Of course there are irregularities, fluctuations, perturbations and short-term inconsistencies but by and large this observation is incontrovertible as we shall see in the balance of this chapter.

Let us take the first step by quickly examining the evidence pertaining to inert matter. In so doing the meaning he attached to the word cosmogenesis will become clear.

Cosmogenesis: The First Phase of Evolution

Interstellar space, so astronomers tell us, consists of an incredibly diffuse 'gas' of hydrogen, the simplest of atoms, or more likely, simpler (less complex) matter—electrons and protons. At any rate the density is so low that the vacuum in space is lower by far than the best vacuum ever produced on earth in a laboratory. Now although astronomers and astral physicists are not in agreement on how stars form, the fact is that they did form at some time in the distant past (and for that matter probably even now are in the process of being born in outer space). Furthermore we know, from studies of the spectra of light emitted by stars, that in them exist atoms of elements heavier than hydrogen. Since a helium atom for example is more than an arbitrarily rounded-off cluster of hydrogen atoms and has properties different from hydrogen, helium is more complex than hydrogen. Therefore in stars the complexity rises. How this happens—the question which science legitimately asks—is just beginning to be understood. Neutron capture, beta decay and helium fusion are undoubtedly the processes taking place in stars and supernovae which produce atoms of the heavy elements and very simple molecules. Regardless of what the mechanisms are the significant point for our purposes is that stars are an aggregation of matter in which the constituent atoms have a higher degree of complexity than in what existed previously.

Proceeding on we come to the planets—ours in particular. Again let's not concern ourselves with how the earth was formed—whether by condensation of a star, by a near collision of two stars tearing off fragments of each which subsequently condensed or by some other mechanism. The important point is that the earth under our feet contains minerals and molecules—complex forms of matter which can't possibly exist in stars because the stars are too hot. Furthermore science tells us that planets form from stars, after them in time. The earth obviously just didn't appear, from nothing, ready made as we know it today. It had a predecessor of some kind which, as near as we know, was a star, or stars, or portion thereof. Whatever it was, that which preceded our planet or any planet certainly ranks lower on the centrated-complexity scale than the material of the planet itself.

From the two preceding paragraphs we can begin to see the universal trend Fr. Teilhard noted in the universe. Even at the level of matter events tend to happen in such a way that more complex 'things' are produced. But note that it is only on planets that this series can progress further and only on some planets which have the proper temperature and gravitational forces could life as we know it ever form by a continuation of the trend. Thus planets instead of being mere insignificant pinpricks in an uncomprehensible vastness, are the only places where this evolutionary trend of increasing centro-complexity can progress. As Fr. Teilhard says, "It is thru them that the axis of life now passes." [9]

The reader has probably noticed an omission up to this point. So far no formal connection has been made between the centrated-complexity scale and the withinness-withoutness scale. It is now time to tie these two together although the relation is surely obvious. Notwithstanding the fact that at this point in time we can't characterize either scale quantitatively, there is a one to one correspondence between the two. More centrated-complexity and a more pronounced within are but two sides of the same coin. In other words Fr. Teilhard is saying that evolution proceeds in such a way that 'things' with more centrated-complexity *and* a more pronounced within tend to form. "Once we take up this point of view—which makes of biology simply the physics of the very highly complex—it is interesting to see how everything included in our experience falls into place: and I mean everything. . . ." [10] With these words of Fr. Teilhard in mind lets continue following the genesis of the world from where we stopped.

What happened on our planet before life appeared? How did life originate? No one knows for sure of course. In a general way, Fr. Teilhard would say that the same trend towards increasing complexity continued. The evolution of matter towards more complexity, cosmic evolution—or cosmogenesis—did not cease when our earth was born. It continued. By some mechanism or another atoms and molecules arranged themselves into ever more complicated arrangements. Simultaneously the within of the large molecules increased. It, the within, finally reached a point in large megamolecules where it became so concentrated and intense that a change in state, or a discrete discontinuity as he calls it, occurred. A quantitative increase caused a qualitative change. Megamolecules changed to microorganisms. Life was born.

It's as though one continuously adds heat to a kettle of water: when the boiling point is reached a change of state occurs—water changes to steam. This analogy of Fr. Teilhard's is quite apt. In fact he even uses the term 'psychic temperature' to describe the intensity of withinness much the way we use temperature as a measure of hotness. Just as, upon the addition of heat, a liquid changes its physical state when the boiling point is reached on the thermal scale, with the unfolding of evolutionary time nonliving matter changed to living matter when a critical psychic temperature was attained on the centrated-complexity (or within/without) scale. And since this could only happen on planets that is why they are so important in the cosmos.

It is fascinating to note how compatible recent

research results on the chemistry of 'prelife' are with Fr. Teilhard's overall view of the cosmos. Many of the intermediate steps between simple molecules and living cells which scientists believe must have occurred billions of years ago have been 'duplicated' in laboratories, principally since Fr. Teilhard's death. In 1952 Stanley Miller assembled a simple glass apparatus into which he put a mixture of water vapor, hydrogen, methane and ammonia—simple molecular gases presumed to have been present on the earth long before life appeared. By subjecting various mixtures to an electrical discharge (such as might have occurred in an electrical storm) he produced amino acids, the building blocks of enzymes and proteins. Since then others have produced similar results with ultra violet radiation. In the early 1960's researchers at the Florida State University mixed up a 'primordial soup' of various amino acids, 'cooked it' under conditions thought to have existed on our infant earth and synthesized large protein-like molecules. At lower temperatures similar results can be obtained if phosphorus is present—an observation especially relevant to the origins of life in view of the importance of ATP (adenosine triphosphate) to life processes.

Even more remarkable, because it is a further major advance in biological research, is the achievement of Mehran Goulian, Arthur Kornberg and Robert Sinsheimer announced shortly before this book went to press. These three Stanford University scientists successfully synthesized biologically active DNA (deoxyribonucleic acid), a virus-like substance. Although this achievement comes close, no one has yet produced 'life in a test tube' or created living cells from inert matter. If we ever do, as I suspect we will someday, it should not come as a shock nor should it undermine anyone's faith in God if he can envision the world as Fr. Teilhard did. As Fr. Teilhard repeatedly said, mankind has enormous undeveloped talents and there seems to be no physical or psychic force of any kind capable of preventing him from seeking, inventing and creating in every domain.

Paleontological evidence pertaining to the exact form of the first living cells or vitalized megamolecules or whatever they were are unavailable to us and always will be. Even when considering more advanced forms of life which leave fossils the first members of the species are always impossible to identify just as the beginning of anything is usually nebulous. It is only when a species becomes sufficiently differentiated and established through evolutionary processes and leaves its remains as fossils that we can recognize and distinguish it from another.

> Beginnings have an irritating but essential fragility, and one that should be taken to heart by all who occupy themselves with history.
>
> It is the same *in every domain:* when anything really new begins to germinate around us, we cannot distinguish it—for the very good reason that it could only be recognized in the light of what it is going to be. Yet, if, when it has reached full growth, we look back to find its starting point, we only find that the starting point itself is now hidden from our view, destroyed or forgotten.[11]

Note the italicized words 'in every domain.' How true this is. Yet how often we forget it? Who can say when printing began? Was it Gutenberg, or the Egyptians and Babylonians with their papyrus, or cave men drawing on the walls of their homes? And what about aeroplanes? Were the Wright brothers first or were they preceded by the "tower jumpers" of the middle ages? Or think of the first Americans. Were our constitution writers first, or the Pilgrims, or the Indians, or those who preceded them? It *is* the same in every domain. Be it technology, civilization, linguistics or anything else the first stages of growth disappear as they recede into the past.

This is not to imply that the transition from non-life to life was a gradual affair. It couldn't have been. However we define life (and this is still a problem as, for example, when considering virus particles) there must have been a distinct change, a discontinuity within the continuity of evolution. Since this idea of discontinuity within continuity is so important to an understanding of Fr. Teilhard's vision and will be of even more significance in the next few pages, it is well to quote him exactly.

> So, in one sense, we can no more fix an absolute zero in time (as was once supposed) for the advent of life than for that of any other experimental reality. On the experimental and phenomenological plane, a given universe and each of its parts can only have one and the same duration, to which there is no backward limit. Thus each thing extends itself and pushes its roots into the past, ever farther back, by that which makes it most itself. Everything, in some extremely attenuated extension of itself, has existed from the very first. Nothing can be done in a direct way to counter this basic condition of our knowledge.
>
> But to have realized and accepted once and for all that each new being has and must have a *cosmic embryogenesis* in no way invalidates the reality of its *historic birth.*
>
> In every domain, when anything exceeds a certain measurement, it suddenly changes its as-

> pect, condition or nature. The curve doubles back, the surface contracts to a point, the solid disintegrates, the liquid boils, the germ cell divides, intuition suddenly bursts on the piled up facts. . . . Critical points have been reached, rungs on the ladder, involving a change of state—jumps of all sorts *in the course* of development. Henceforward this is the *only* way in which science can speak of a 'first instant.' But it is none the less a *true* way.[12]

With the advent of life evolution entered upon a new phase—biological evolution or biogenesis—because only in this way could the 'stuff' of the universe acquire more centrated-complexity in accordance with the universal evolutionary trend Fr. Teilhard saw. This is not to say that prebiological evolution, cosmogenesis, abruptly ceased; it is probably still going on. But we should leave it and devote attention now to the subsequent phase because it is of more interest.

Biogenesis: The Second Phase of Evolution

In a historical sense we associate the beginning of modern evolutionary theory with Charles Darwin. Since his time a little over a hundred years ago our knowledge of evolution has continued to increase. And it is doing so at an accelerating rate each year if we judge the rate of increase of knowledge by the number of scientific papers published and/or the number of paleontologists, biologists, ecologists and other specialists studying hereditary mechanisms and other aspects of evolutionary change. Fr. Teilhard made many contributions to the field. For example, he was one of the paleontologists who worked on and at the site where Peking man was discovered (this is still the best documented example of Homo Erectus). Many of his papers and essays describe this, and other, specific details of biological evolution.

Because it is not essential that one understand the complex details of evolution in order to comprehend Fr. Teilhard's theory and because biological evolution is only a part of the total picture the specifics are not offered here. I should say however that it is my distinct impression, obtained from occasional reading of general interest articles and verified by conversations with university colleagues in various fields, that nothing discovered since Fr. Teilhard's death invalidates his concept. Perhaps a few strictly scientific details which he described are no longer generally accepted but there are no new findings which refute his work. In fact, considered in a broad context, the very fact that we are in the midst of the so-called knowledge explosion reinforces my belief that Fr. Teilhard's vision is a true vision of reality.

Even though I am not going to attempt to describe the process of biological evolution in detail it will be helpful to look at a diagram (Figure 1) representing the tree of life in a highly schematic form because it illustrates an important point. On the diagram time is represented vertically. Sometime after the advent of life (some three billion years ago according to the latest thinking) living cells on our planet began to diversify due to differences in environment, hereditary changes and selections. And so a splitting into different kinds of organisms occurred. These splittings are represented on the sketch by branchings.

Not explicitly represented on the figure is the fact that as evolution progressed cells began to associate with one another, first, perhaps, loosely in 'rounded-off aggregates' but later, certainly, in 'organized wholes.' Multicelled organisms or metazoa in which each cell pays a vital role in an interdependent complex of cells appeared. Much as atoms had become associated to form molecules at an earlier stage of evolution, cells united to form metazoa at a later stage. Thus the trend towards increasing centro-complexity continued with the passing of time by the same type of phenomenon as that observed during cosmogenesis, namely by the coalescence and uniting of elements of lower complexity.

Some of the branchings in Figure 1 represent diversification into metazoa. And the branchings of these represent further diversification–into kingdoms, phyla, subphyla, classes, orders, families, genera, species and subspecies. Many of the organisms and creatures which nature tried were not adaptable to their environment and hence became extinct; dinosaurs are an example. But many others have survived. We know that today the biosphere, that relatively thin region near the surface of the earth in which all living beings exist, includes plants of an almost infinite variety –trees, shrubs, grasses, lichens, mushrooms, algae –a host of animal forms–mammals, marsupials, birds, fishes, reptiles, insects, worms, mollusks– plus thousands of tiny one-celled organisms which are difficult to classify in either the animal or vegetable kingdom. Branching is still occurring today; so also are species becoming extinct. The number of different kinds of living beings which have existed and/or are living on our planet and

EVOLUTIONARY TIME UNFOLDS
IN THIS DIRECTION
Advent of life

FIGURE I

the complex hereditary relationships between them truly stagger the imagination.

Also not shown on Figure 1 is the fact that the milieu in which different living 'things' existed has changed with geological and climatic changes. The stage upon which the play of life is progressing has a continually changing backdrop.

With this broad picture in our mind the obvious question is "Was life, say up to the end of the Tertiary period (one or two million years ago in round numbers), going anywhere?" The question is not whether there is an evolution of one sort or another. It's existence is so well established now that to deny it is absurd. But whether or not evolution is *directed*, whether there is any reason to it, any pattern behind it, is another question. With notable exceptions most biologists and evolutionists today will say no, even passionately. Books and articles are still being written by eminent scientists in which they flatly deny any kind of teleological interpretation of evolution. In their eyes man is just another species of animal doomed to eventual extinction without any trace of him surviving in the universe.

In sharp contrast to this belief Fr. Teilhard affirms that there is an *axis* and a *direction*. It can be seen provided we look beyond, or rather *within*, the external phenomena and try to see that everything has an inner nature.

The reason that Fr. Teilhard believes that most biologists can not see the general trend underlying all of evolution is that they are too preoccupied with morphological details and mechanisms, that is, with the without of organisms, and are not considering the within of the living beings. The difference is in the way of looking at the facts, not in the facts themselves. The contrast between the two approaches can be illustrated by the following example. According to the thinking of those who oppose Fr. Teilhard's interpretation, a tiger, for instance, develops its carnivorous instincts *because* it inherits from its parents cutting molars and sharp claws. Fr. Teilhard argues that this proposition should be turned around. In other words he says that if the tiger elongates its fangs and sharpens its claws it is because the tiger, following its line of descent, receives from its parents the 'soul of a carnivore' and this in turn is why it develops the external characteristics it does. Note that this line of reasoning asserts that the within (instincts, 'soul of carnivore') determines the without (teeth, claws) and not vice versa. Fr. Teilhard does not dismiss the value of studying external factors but he does say that if we look only at the without of 'things' we will never be able to understand evolution.

> It must be maintained that scholars are abundantly right in setting a high value on the marks life makes on living flesh, or leaves on fossilized remains. But let them beware, in the course of their work, not to lose or even to reverse the sense of the values they are considering. It is not the tissues and bones that have made living creatures. Bones and tissues are only the shells in which psychic tendencies have successively clothed themselves; and these tendencies were the product always of the same fundamental aspiration to know and act.[13]

The approach exemplified by this example and quotation is the path Fr. Teilhard follows in untangling the tree of life, making sense of it and confirming his belief that *all* of evolution follows the same general trend. The foundation for understanding how he does this has already been laid. All that needs to be done is build upon it.

In living organisms we come to a problem in evaluating high degrees of centrated-complexity. A virus particle for example has a molecular weight in excess of 1,000,000. A mammal has approximately 100 billion cells each containing hundreds of millions of atoms. When considering these 'things' number of atoms, molecules and cells are really of minor importance compared with the number and quality of *links* established between the atoms, molecules and cells. Fr. Teilhard's reason behind this thinking is that numbers (of atoms) are primarily a measure of the without. At the lower stages of evolution this procedure was satisfactory, but what is needed now is a more realistic parameter by which to gauge the within.

His solution is simple. He asked the question: How do we judge the centrated-complexity of a being? Phrased this way there can be only one answer—by the extent to which its nervous system is developed. The only logical parameter by which we can gage the degree of centeredness of a living being is by the complexity and development of its brain and nerves. As the centrated-complexity of a being increases so does that of its nervous system and vice versa. There is a one to one correlation between the two. And as the nervous system's complexity increases so does the awareness and consciousness of its owner. True, complexity of the nervous system, or consciousness, is a parameter presently impossible to express by meaningful numbers but this is no reason for not selecting what is assuredly a correct solution to the problem at hand.

In effect all this amounts to is a change of scale.

It is a common procedure which we all employ when necessary. Who would use a ruler to measure the mileage between Philadelphia and New York or an automobile odometer to determine whether a new piece of furniture would fit through a doorway? In both cases we want to measure a distance and so we use the logical measuring device for the job at hand. In an analogous way he changed the measuring 'device' on his centrated-complexity scale from an easily visualized physical parameter to one less easy to measure quantitatively but one which is, nevertheless, more appropriate. To reflect this change in parameter applicable to living beings Fr. Teilhard also changed the name of the scale–from centrated-complexity to complexity-consciousness, but the principle remains the same.

Following this lead, the axis of evolution becomes clearly defined, as does its direction. There is a logical and consistent pattern to both cosmogenesis and biogenesis. Just as cosmogenesis proceeded to its 'boiling point,' at which point matter in the form of large megamolecules changed its state to living matter, so, Fr. Teilhard argues, biological evolution proceeded along an analogous path. The leading shoot of biological evolution was in that group of living organisms in which the nervous system was most fully developed. Again omitting the paleontological and biological details and a discussion of the mechanisms, this Ariadne's Thread as Fr. Teilhard calls it in *The Phenomenon of Man,* leads up to the great apes at the end of the Tertiary period. In them the within became concentrated and intensified, because they had the best developed nervous system, to the point where another change of state, quantum jump, or discrete discontinuity occurred. This was the birth of reflective life. Man *as*cended from the apes, he didn't descend.

One can use Figure 1 to get a simplified view of how Fr. Teilhard pictured the immense complexity of biological evolution and the emergence of man. (I should forewarn the reader that what follows is my analogy, not Fr. Teilhard's.) Visualize the tree of life as a growing plant: it grows, in time, by branching—the diversification of living beings already mentioned. Statistical factors, the play of large numbers and chance mutations certainly played a major role in determining the detailed appearance of the tree of life as did environmental factors.

A growing plant needs light to grow so picture a light above the top of the figure but with a translucent membrane inserted between the light and the growing plant. The membrane transmits some light but it is a soft diffuse light of equal intensity everywhere. The membrane represents a barrier to growth in the sense that if a shoot of the growing plant (tree of life) could penetrate this barrier it would enter a bright new world unknown to it before. Now further visualize that each growing shoot on the tree of life has a different temperature. (Admittedly my analogy is a bit contrived here since the growing buds on actual plants probably do not vary in temperature, but still, it will help if we can visualize that they do.) The different temperatures in different growing shoots represent the idea that different living species had different psychic temperatures; that is—some were more aware than others, or, in practical terms, some had better developed nervous systems than others. Now as evolution proceeded the tree of life grew in an apparently haphazard fashion due to chance mutations, etc.

As it developed, different shoots, at different temperatures, butted up against the barrier. Most of them could grow no further. But one shoot which had developed by a particularly favorable combination of chance circumstances had an unusually high (psychic) temperature. It melted the membrane, broke through the barrier, and immediately a completely new range of possibilities for future growth was available to it.

Without having gone into the technicalities, that analogy expresses what I think to be the gist of Fr. Teilhard's ideas with respect to biological evolution and the origin of man. It incorporates by extension of the analogy

> a double series of mutually balanced considerations that fall under two heads:
>
> 1. In the eyes of science, the appearance of man followed, essentially, the same mechanism (geographical and morphological) as every other species.
> 2. Nevertheless, right from his origins, we find in man certain special properties, that denote in him a higher vitality than we meet in any other species.[14]

The shoot (in my analogy) which broke through the membrane represents the primates from which man evolved. "In this singular and privileged case, the particular orthogenesis of the phylum happened to coincide exactly with the principal orthogenesis of life itself." [15]

A question which inevitably comes to people's minds at this point should be discussed. It is variously phrased but always comes down to the following, "What did Fr. Teilhard say about monogenism vs. polygenism? Did he believe there was one Adam or many Adams?" Because this question has so many emotional and religious overtones it would be best to quote him exactly rather than try to paraphrase his thoughts.

> Thus *in the eyes of science,* which at long range can only see things in bulk, the 'first man' is, and can only be, a *crowd,* and his infancy is made up of thousands and thousands of years. That is why the problem of monogenism in the strict sense of the words seems to *elude* science as such by its very nature. At those depths of time when hominisation took place [read—when man first appeared], the presence and the movements of a unique couple are positively ungraspable, unrevealable to our eyes at no matter what magnification. Accordingly one can say that there is room *in this interval* for anything that a trans-experimental source of knowledge might demand.[16]

Two pages later in *The Phenomenon of Man* the following paragraph and footnote appear. (Both below and immediately above I have incorporated a paragraph and a footnote into single paragraphs.)

> In light of these considerations, and particularly when dealing with a group as homogeneous and specialized as the one under discussion, I feel inclined to minimize the effects of parallelism in the initial formation of the human branch. On the verticil of the higher primates, this branch did not, in my opinion, glean its fibers here and there, one by one, from the whole range offered: but, even more closely than any other species, this branch, I am convinced, represents the thickening and successful development of one solitary stem among all—this stem being, moreover, the most central of the collection because the most vital and, except for the brain, the least specialized. If that is right, all human lines join up genetically, but at the bottom, at the very point of reflection. Which amounts to saying that if the science of

> man can say nothing directly for or against monogenism (a single couple—see [previous quote]) it can on the other hand come out decisively, it seems, in favor of monophyletism (a single phylum).[17]

The reader may be disturbed by the observation that Fr. Teilhard doesn't seem to have made a definitive statement one way or the other regarding the 'problem' of monogenism or polygenism. As I pointed out in Chapter 1 when referring to Fr. North's book this problem and the related one concerning original sin haven't yet been solved from either a scientific *or* theological standpoint. I believe that when the full story is known, if it is ever known, both science and religion will agree because, after all, truth cannot contradict truth. Any *apparent* disagreement at the present time arises because of our inability as humans to perceive the total truth in either sphere of knowledge. "In the meantime the proper attitude for the believer cannot be in doubt. He has merely to seek, patiently and confidently, *on both sides.* Faith guarantees that there can be no contradiction between his creed and human knowledge."[18]

* * * * * *

According to the second item in Fr. Teilhard's summary we have now come to a half way point. We have described his evolutionary law of complexity-consciousness and seen how both cosmic and biological evolution exhibit similar characteristics in light of this law. Cosmogenesis produced more complex forms of matter and culminated in life when the within reached an appropriately high level. Biogenesis led to more conscious biological organisms and culminated in man when the psychic temperature reached another critical point. In both cases evolutionary progress was made by the coalescence of elemental units into a 'closed whole' of a 'higher' form.

Fr. Teilhard was not a mere cataloguer of facts but a scientist who was trying to comprehend the phenomena of evolution as deeply and completely as he could. He was trying to build a theory of evolution which would be all inclusive and he therefore recognized that there must be something common to all phases of evolution which causes the law of complexity-consciousness to hold in completely different 'spheres' of evolution —as he believed it did. More than that, he *knew* that there had to be something—a flux, a force field of some kind, so to speak—which was ultimately responsible for the fact that so many seemingly unrelated phenomena (we have discussed only a portion of them so far) could be understood within the context of one law of nature. And so he postulated a unifying concept and called it radial energy. It is a concept of reality which is more fundamental than the law of centrated-complexity-consciousness because it is the cause of the law; it is that which makes the evolutionary law be a law of nature.

Since the discussion thus far in this chapter has used the law of complexity-consciousness as a basis for describing evolution up to man, it is obvious that Fr. Teilhard's concept of radial energy has been implicitly included. But to continue the development, to see the nature and consequences of the major evolutionary breakthrough which occurred when man appeared on the scene it will be necessary to use his notion of radial energy (and its counterpart, tangential energy) more explicitly.

The Two Energies

Energy, according to Fr. Teilhard, exists in two forms, tangential and radial.

By tangential energy he means all those forms of energy with which we are familiar. Tangential is a generic adjective which includes all those other adjectives by which scientists and engineers ordinarily classify energy: potential, kinetic, mechanical, chemical, electrical, hydroelectric, thermal, nuclear or any one of a number of other categories which suit our convenience. Tangential energy is associated with the without of things and is measurable by means of calorimeters and assorted other instruments. With the exception that we can never assign an absolute value to it, it is completely definable in terms of our four dimensional space-time. It is, as Fr. Teilhard says, the "energy which links the element with all others of the same order . . . as itself in the universe."[19] That is to say, it is involved in reactions between 'things' at the same position along the centrated-complexity-consciousness scale.

Radial energy on the other hand is associated with the within of 'things'; it links elements of different order within the universe. It is energy associated with the intangible and is therefore spiritual in nature. In the language of physics and chemistry radial energy manifests itself as the driving force of evolution. In short it is what makes the cosmos evolve. It is that which is pushing and pulling—causing—directing the cosmic process in an irreversible fashion.

To some people with a scientific background

this idea of radial energy sounds very strange. Many feel an instinctive repugnance against any scientific scheme of causality. In fact it is positively repulsive to some scientists. "It's anti-scientific" is a typical reaction. What is really meant is—"If you can't possibly prove that there is a radial energy by scientific experimentation (which no one can, by experimentation) it's not a valid hypothesis and I won't believe it because it's not subject to proof. I base my science on cold hard observable facts and nothing else. Science has no place for fuzzy thinking and spiritual 'magic.' Therefore Fr. Teilhard's ideas must be wrong, to put it politely."

I should like to discuss this type of criticism because it bothers a good many people, most of whom I am convinced are sincere. Since the discussion is rather involved and diverts us from the main thrust of this chapter, it is given in Appendix 1. There the reader may find my arguments which show that Fr. Teilhard's concept of the two energies is not incompatible with the science of energy, thermodynamics. The principal points may be summarized as follows:

1. One of the foundation stones of present day thermodynamics is expressible by the sentence: 'It is impossible to reverse any natural process in its entirety.' Another is: 'Thermodynamics cannot say anything about how the universe is behaving.'
2. The thermodynamics of today (i.e., that built upon statement 1) is concerned only with tangential energy because this is the only kind which is experimentally knowable.
3. No one can prove that there is not another way of knowing. (In fact many people

believe there are definitely other ways of knowing.)

4. Scientific observation shows that entropy inevitably increases.
5. Evolution
   a) appears to be irreversible, and
   b) moving in the direction of the rise and expansion of consciousness.
6. Fr. Teilhard is proposing a new 'kind' of energy, radial energy,
   a) which is not handleable by our present day thermodynamics because it is not experimentally and quantitatively measureable, and
   b) which drives the universe in an irreversible fashion
   c) antientropically, i.e., towards Life.

The reader must decide for himself whether or not these statements and my arguments leading up to them are incompatible and if he thinks Fr. Teilhard's theory is antiscientific or not. I don't think so. Quite to the contrary, I'd say they are most concordant and that his theory is suprascientific. More than that, I think Fr. Teilhard's theory is one of the most remarkable and most hopeful ever conceived by the human mind. He is saying that radial energy is increasing and more than compensates for 'wasted' tangential energy, or entropy. The energy of the universe is not conserved, is not a static quantity which will eventually be 'used up'—rather the energy of the universe is forever increasing. The universe is not static, nor is it dying; it is dynamic, it is living and growing more alive every day. Furthermore, as we shall see later, man can help it become more alive by the actions of his free will.

The Third Phase of Evolution: Noogenesis

Without and within, law of complexity-consciousness and the two energies—these are the three interrelated elements of Fr. Teilhard's vision. But the most fundamental of all is radial energy because it is that mysterious force which causes 'things' to become more complex thereby raising their psychic temperature or intensity of withinness as time passes on. Radial energy caused the planet earth to form and was affecting it long before life appeared. It caused granules of matter—atoms—to assume ever more complicated structural arrangements until finally the psychic temperature became so high that *matter became vitalized.* Granules of life—cells—appeared. The radial energy flux, being an inherent and inescapable part of our universe, did not cease to influence evolution then. As it always had, it continued to operate and caused granules of life to coalesce, combine and form ever more complex organisms. A countless myriad of different arrangements of cells (viz.,—different species) occurred under its influence with the further passage of time. Finally, in one particular type of animal which happened to have an opposed thumb, could walk upright and, most important of all, had the largest brain, the psychic temperature reached another critical point. *Life became hominized* (to use another word coined by Fr. Teilhard). Granules of thought were born. That is what we humans are, 'granules of thought'!

As one might suspect, Fr. Teilhard says that the radial energy flux didn't stop then either. It kept right on influencing evolution and continues to affect us granules of thought much as it did granules of life and granules of matter in times past, oftentimes unnoticeably but always irresistibly. But we should take one step at a time and, as before, look at the phenomena and examine the evidence to try to see how and in what direction the universal tide is carrying us.

The first step obviously is to differentiate between men and animals. It is perhaps superfluous to mention that there are some people today who deny that man is qualitatively different from the animals. They'll acknowledge that he's more intelligent, but to them he's an intelligent animal and not a creature who is different in some essential way. "After all," they argue, "what basis do you have for saying that human intelligence is not just a highly developed instinct? What rational reason is there for saying that man is more highly developed than a bee or an orchid or a dolphin? Isn't each nothing more than the most highly developed species on its respective branch of the tree of life? Couldn't man be just a passing wave in the evolutionary sequence and therefore only be dominating the earth temporarily as dinosaurs did in the Mesozioc Era?"

Fortunately, I think, this kind of thinking is on the wane. Most modern anthropologists regardless of their religious beliefs, even when studying the most primitive tribes of people living today, recognize in them a distinctive quality characteristic of all other members of the species homo sapiens and not merely a quantitative difference between them and the higher animals.

Nevertheless, since there are still some who, even in 1968, cannot see this difference (which corresponds to the change in state which occurred when a shoot of the tree of life broke through the membrane in my analogy) it is in order to amplify the point and explain Fr. Teilhard's line of reasoning.

He believed it was necessary to settle the question not only for scientific reasons but also for the sake of ethics of life. And he saw only one way to do it. That was to brush aside all external factors (similarity of men to animals in a physiological sense) and secondary considerations (instinct in men and animals for example) and make straight for the central phenomenon which, he and all other Christians and many others believe, distinguishes man from the animals. The power of *reflection* is this central phenomenon. I can think of no better way to describe the meaning of this term concisely than in Fr. Teilhard's own words.

> Reflection is, as the word indicates, the power acquired by a consciousness to turn inward upon itself, to take possession of itself *as of an object* endowed with its own particular consistence and value: no longer merely to know, but to know oneself; no longer merely to know but to know that one knows.[20]

A creature possessing the power of reflection is a different *kind* of being (compared to those not possessing this talent) because it lives in a different dimension, that of reflective life. The reflective being can perform mental abstractions, reason with the use of logic, synthesize thoughts and invent, calculate in the dimensions of space and time, love and appreciate and understand intangibles. He can also worry, develop anxieties and tensions, and fear death because he realizes that there may be something after death. All these activities of the *inner life* are nothing more than a manifestation of the reflective center in man, viz. his soul, as it *im*plodes upon itself. In short man is the only creature who asks himself—"Who am I?"

These arguments and numerous others like them in Fr. Teilhard's writings ought to convince anyone, I should think, that man transcends the animal kingdom. He lives within a different domain, the domain of reflective thought, while at the same time maintaining his biological ties to the animals. If it makes some people any happier Fr. Teilhard, in one of his books, said something to the effect that the first men (man) probably looked like apes but they obviously were not apes because the significant change was in the within, not the without. In another place he drew attention to the fact that if any animals on the earth had the ability to reflect they certainly wouldn't have escaped our attention.

The passage just quoted and the arguments just given were taken from Fr. Teilhard's 'apologetic' works. *The Phenomenon of Man* and many of his other essays are among these. They were written primarily for atheists and agnostics. He was trying to show them that his view of the cosmos incorporated the best of their aspirations yet went beyond theirs. Because he was trying to reach unbelievers he naturally didn't want to use the word God in his arguments. Fr. Teilhard was a deeply religious man however and in several of his 'nonapologetic' works left no doubt that the most basic difference he saw between men and animals is that man is a creature who has the ability to perceive God whereas animals don't have this capability. The ability to perceive God or lack of it is the principal distinguishing characteristic between the two orders of life. The significant issue, at this point in our outline of Fr. Teilhard's theory, therefore, is whether or not man *has* the ability to perceive God, not whether or not he *uses* it. Again, the reader must decide for himself whether or not man *has* this ability.

One of Fr. Teilhard's unusual intellectual talents was his ability to mentally look at the universe from outside, as it were. Thus, in order to comprehend his message we must try to do the same. That means that we must try to look at the world from an evolutionary perspective. We must think not only in terms of evolutionary time but also try to develop an evolutionary sense of space, of depth, of number, of proportion, of quality, of movement, of duration. In addition we must try to develop a sense of the organic, which is to say that we must try to see the similarities (the differences are obvious) between different orders of things, the structural parallelisms among 'things' at different positions along the centrated-complexity scale. It will help us see the world the way Fr. Teilhard did if we can learn to view everything as part of a process with a purpose and realize that different portions of the whole are at different stages in the process at any given time.

Let us try to do this in looking at the phenomenon of man since he first appeared on the earth a million and a half years ago. In so doing we will gloss over relatively minor details, just as we did in studying cosmogenesis and biogenesis. 'Relatively minor details' as used here may cover several hundred years, as the rise and fall of whole civilizations, wars, and such. All that I am trying to do in this chapter is to paint the overall picture, omitting the details. (In the next chapter, however I will discuss what I believe to be the most important 'detail' of Fr. Teilhard's theory.)

Before trying to describe continuing evolution as Fr. Teilhard thought it to be occurring today one other idea, which is new and yet not new, must be introduced. The essence of the idea can be expressed in the following form: *Fr. Teilhard assigned a positive evolutionary value to the social phenomena around us.* Incorporation of this new-old thought into the body of ideas already discussed is all that is needed to complete the story and thereby understand why, to many people, Fr. Teilhard's vision is simultaneously a theoretical system encompassing all of man's knowledge, a rule for action which can resolve man's problems, a profound expression of Christianity and a plausible prediction of the near and far future.

The question before us now is: "Has man reached the end of the evolutionary line, is he the apex of life?" Fr. Teilhard says that most (but not all) scientists, sociologists and philosophers either tacitly assume or explicitly assert that man has reached a final and supreme stage of humanity beyond which he can not possibly advance, that he is the ultimate epitome of evolution. Most of us have read books and articles or heard lectures which confirm this impression. But the fact is that there is absolutely no proof of any kind (scientific, philosophical or religious) that man has reached his full potential. "On the contrary," Fr. Teilhard says, "everything suggests that at the present time we are entering a peculiarly critical phase of super-humanization." [21] To illustrate the point he likened evolution to a multi-stage rocket in which the initial stage carries it to a certain point after which the successive stages take over and, one after another, push it to higher planes (of altitude in the case of rockets, of consciousness in the case of evolution). "Like one of those multiple stage rockets, (evolution) is *now* (my italics) visibly starting a fresh forward leap, with a directive mechanism and a power of penetration that are both fundamentally new." [22]

Superhumanization of man and the evolutionary value of society—these are two sides of the same coin by which we can understand post-biological evolution. I'll attempt to make the relation clearer by discussing man's environment, man as an individual and then society—all from the evolutionary point of view.

Geologists tell us that the surface of the earth itself has changed considerably since man appeared and continues to change. Mountains have turned to plains, ice ages have come and gone, weathering and slowly varying climatic changes have significantly altered our environment over a period of time. During the same period paleontologists and biologists have watched the coming and going of various species of plant and animal life. All of these environmental factors have affected man—his domiciles, clothing, food, methods of living, art forms, religions—and they can not be neglected. However . . . extensive though these changes in the lithosphere and biosphere may have been in the past or might be in the future, they must be of secondary importance if we envisage the universe as Fr. Teilhard did. Thought, reflective thought, is the culmination of all evolution. It just doesn't make sense therefore from Fr. Teilhard's perspective, to say that whether we live on Atlantis or North America, whether we eat mastadons or steers, whether we wear bearskins or Fifth Avenue styles is really going to make much difference in the long run. In other words, if we want to predict the future based on the past we shouldn't look at the earth or its plant and animal life; we should look at man and see what is happening to him because he is the only creature whose within has evolved to the point of reflection.

With these thoughts in mind we'll leave man's environment and look at man himself.

Scientists really don't know whether the without of man's first ancestors was much different from our without. Part of the problem of course, which we've already seen, is the impossibility of scientifically identifying our first ancestors. Another part of the problem is that the time span since our origins probably hasn't been long enough to have produced marked changes in our physique. From a short range standpoint it seems to be established that the younger generation is bigger and stronger than their parents—at least in the United States—but this really isn't a fair sampling by which to judge on an evolutionary time scale. The fact that people come in different colors—black, white, yellow, red, brown—is one indication that *maybe* the without of man has changed. But we shall as surely be led astray from understanding evolution as Hitler was with his theories of the master race if we look for the course of future evolution in the external characteristics of man. Because evolution entered a new sphere with the birth of thought we must try to see if any change in the within of men, considered individually and collectively has or is occurring.

And so we leave the without of man and direct our attention to the within.

It is important to recognize that our earliest human ancestors had the same fundamental characteristics as any one of us living in the latter half of the twentieth century. Stated in Fr. Teilhard's terminology it is the power of reflection; phrased according to Christian teaching it is the immortal soul created in the image and likeness of God. This is not to say however that the within of man has not changed.

Certainly no one needs to be convinced that the average man of today knows more than his predecessors knew. We, *as individuals,* have stored in our minds an immensely greater amount of knowledge and ideas than our forebears did—spoken and written languages, mathematical, scientific, philosophic and religious ideas, and so forth. These have evolved over the ages and are passed on from generation to generation partly perhaps by internal factors (biological hereditary mechanisms) and partly by external factors such as education for example. Fr. Teilhard thought that both Lamarckian and Darwinian factors played an important role in the rise of consciousness.

It is worthwhile to reflect for a moment on the slow progress by which man has advanced to his present state. We'll never know exactly when he first appeared on the scene but it's approximately one and a half million years ago according to recent scientific estimates. One and a half million years is a long time but it's only a small fraction of one percent of the age of the earth and only a slightly larger fraction of the time that life itself has existed on the earth. Within this 'short' period of one and a half million years we estimate that it took on the order of 500,000 years for communication ability and the necessary involutions of the cerebral cortex to evolve to a state which we could call speech. The origins of man's use of fire are still hidden but probably started about a million years ago at about the time speech became developed, but not necessarily in the same place. At first fire was used as protection from the cold and wild animals, and only much later for cooking. Early homo sapiens seem to have been established as a species about a quarter of a million years ago and Neanderthal man came later, 50 to 100,000 years ago. The first indications of a religious belief can be found in burial sites which we would date about fifty thousand years ago. Approximately 25,000 years ago all the primitive forms of man had died out or become absorbed by the more progressive and modern Cromagnon man. The earliest signs of agriculture occur in fossil beds dating no more than ten or fifteen thousand years ago. The era we call historical, for which we have records, is no more than perhaps five or ten thousand years—a half of a percent of the age of man. Looked at from this perspective the 2000 years since Christ, the 200 years of the industrial revolution and the 20 years of the atomic age are seen to be rather insignificant, if that's all we look at.

Primitive man certainly knew more about some things than we do. For example he knew enough to survive in the grasslands and forests of his day. It is the exceptionally rare man of today who can survive in the wilderness for even a few weeks without our modern conveniences and aids. But nevertheless it seems obvious that man is becoming more aware of his environment, more conscious of his place in nature, more spiritual one might say as time passes on. Within the dimension of reflective thought, which is what makes a man a man, an evolution is progressing and has been ever since man appeared over a millenia ago. Each one of us is becoming more aware, and therefore more human, as we learn more, reflect upon it, and incorporate this new knowledge into our within.

An aspect of evolutionary progress by which men become more human is sometimes forgotten. Notice that it is *only* because man is a social creature that he is, *individually,* becoming more knowledgeable and therefore more aware and therefore more human. On the phenomenological level everything that any one of us knows is derived ultimately from the knowledge of others—our contemporaries and those who preceded us. (Even on the supernatural level any knowledge we might have comes from another Person.) A study of the history of anything will prove this. As an example consider our knowledge of the structure of matter and of the work of the countless men that has gone into its development. Think of the evolution of the way of thinking about matter, of the experiments and insights which have led to modern concepts of subatomic structure ('big' physics because it costs so much to build huge accelerators and nuclear reactors), of electronic and atomic structure and the periodic table of elements, of chemical bonding, solid state physics, metallurgy (I had to use the word at least once in this book since I'm a metallurgist by profession!), of the new products, devices and machines being created daily as a result of our increased understanding of matter. Or, to switch to a different domain, think of evolution and the evolution of the idea of evolution. Think of the evolution of the universe and of the solar system, of all the millions upon millions of fossils scattered over the face of the earth, of the progress made in their classification, of the relation between speciation, environmental factors and geological changes, and of the closely related and relatively new field of biochemistry with all its emphasis on DNA, RNA, hereditary mechanisms, etc. Surely no man on earth *alone* could evolve them, nor can any man encompass, master or exhaust them. Yet everyone of us, to different degrees, share, *in our individual consciousness,* in the universal heightening of consciousness. Each one of us as a person is a recipient of, participates in and contributes to the worldwide growth in knowledge and awareness.

> It is only when opposed to other men that the individual can discover his own depth and wholeness. However personal and uncommunicable it may be at its root and origin, reflection can only be developed in communion with others. It is essentially a social phenomena.[23]

Let us briefly recapitulate Fr. Teilhard's arguments up to this point. By a long process of cosmic and biological evolution, which science tells us proceeds by an ascent to the more improbable and which Fr. Teilhard says is caused by a radial energy flux, man evolved from the animal kingdom about one and a half million years ago. Man however is a different kind of creature than the animals from whom he derived his without because he can reflect, that is, he can turn inwards upon himself. Since the within of man is his most important and distinguishing mark and because we are interested in extrapolating, if possible, the cosmic curve of evolution to its end, environmental factors and variations in the without of men are of secondary importance compared to the development of their within. Finally we have seen that individual man has the same essential quality that his earliest ancestors had but that it is developed to a much higher degree in modern man because of the influence of other men.

And now, having brought other men into the

picture, it is time to look at society and its evolution.

The history of mankind, when viewed in bold outline, reveals that the sphere of influence of the individual over other men invariably enlarges as history unfolds. In prehistoric times, when there weren't many men around, the individual only influenced and was influenced by members of his family or tribe. But as he increased in numbers the sphere of influence haltingly but surely expanded—to neighboring tribes, then to the nation (I have in mind North American Indian nations), then to the geographical limits of various land masses in the world. Now the sphere of mutual influence extends throughout the whole world and is becoming more intense every day as our means of communication and transportation improve. It's as though each intellectual (and physical) contact between persons leaves a trace, like a spider's thread. As time passes on the web grows, always becoming more complex and tying persons together in ever more complicated and interrelated patterns. The phenomenon as it exists in the world today is apparent to all and calls for no detailed explanation. As Fr. Teilhard says,

> It takes the form of the all-encompassing ascent of the masses; the constant tightening of economic bonds; the spread of financial and intellectual associations; the totalization of political regimes; the closer physical contact of individuals as well as nations; the increasing impossibility of being or acting or thinking *alone*—in short, the rise, in every form of the *other* around us. We are all constantly aware of these tentacles of a social condition that is rapidly evolving to the point of becoming monstrous.[24]

If one stops to think of it, this whole process

of concentration and growing awareness arises because man is increasing in numbers on a planet of finite size. If our earth were planar and of limitless extent, as our forebears of not too long ago thought, then it is a moot question whether man ever would have evolved, or if he had, if he ever would have developed to his present degree of awareness.

But the earth isn't infinite in extent and we are becoming more conscious. . . . Perhaps then it isn't 'an accident' that we people were born and seem to be getting more compressed every day! Or—is man just a passing wave doomed to oblivion? Does the fact that our living space has a very real limit which we are rapidly approaching mean that sooner or later man is going to end up literally fighting other men for standing space, if he can find enough food to enable him to stand?

For the pessimists there *appears* to be every sort of reason to make gloomy predictions about the future of man. These pessimists, whether they realize it or not, are saying that the whole of evolution is a farce. It has proceeded over countless millions of years, culminating in beings like themselves who can think and reflect, and then, they say, it's all going to end in death. In effect they are saying that life is a joke and we're the victims. Some, but not all, of the pessimists then further conclude that since we're at the end of the line we might as well give up and get whatever pleasure we can out of life before it's too late.

Fr. Teilhard devoted his entire life to combatting these defeatist and pessimistic attitudes. His books are full of eloquent passages in which he tries to show us that we are wrong, dead wrong, if we think that death—utter, complete and total death—is the only way out for the future of man.

In the interests of brevity I will give just one quotation to illustrate the point.

> May I remark once more how ill such a perspective (however much it is favored by those who for all sorts of reasons do not want to see the world around them, and still less man, in process of movement) agrees with the extraordinary vitality of an animal group, which appears by all its characteristics to be, on the contrary, in the full flight of expansion and organization? Never on earth before has such a quantity of living matter reached so high a state of fermentation. How then can they convince us that it is here, in this (human) mass precisely, raised to boiling-point that the forces of speciation have been suddenly extinguished? This is absurd.[25]

What Fr. Teilhard tried to show us is that the social phenomena around us are precisely what one would expect from a study of evolution. In the same way that grains of matter were driven by the radial energy flux to form grains of life, in the same way that grains of life coalesced to form grains of thought under the influence of the evolutionary tide, Fr. Teilhard has shown us that we humans are inevitably *converging* upon one another—*on the mental level.* The driving force is the same and the mechanism is similar; only now convergence is not at the level of matter, nor of (biological) life, but in the dimension of reflective life—thought—spirit. What we are witnessing and are a part of is the progressive formation of more complex, interrelated and interdependent social institutions of all kinds at the highest level of life which evolution has so far produced. Seen in this light social phenomena are nothing more than a continuation of the principle of centrated-complexity-consciousness which has guided evolution from the beginning. And, as before, its logical extension is leading, he believed, to a still higher form of life.

The process of the progressive growth of a sort of thinking envelope surrounding our earth and involving all mankind is what Fr. Teilhard meant by the term noogenesis. It comes from the Greek word 'noos' meaning mind and 'genesis.' It means 'the coming into being of man' and expresses the idea that man is evolving in a manner quite analogous to the way matter evolved in cosmogenesis and life in biogenesis. Fr. Teilhard also invented the word noosphere to denote that layer outside and above, in a transcendental sense, the biosphere which the mental faculties of all men is gradually weaving under the influence of radial energy.

Fr. Tielhard's chapters on the phenomenon of noogenesis are fascinating reading. In one chapter of *The Future of Man* he draws an analogy between the structure and organization of modern society and the anatomy and physiology of, say, a person. In it he likens all forms of education used by mankind to pass on its culture (tradition, languages, schools, libraries, museums, laws and customs, religions, philosophy, science) to the hereditary processes in our bodies. The evolution of tools and machines by which mankind extends his physical capabilities are compared with the mechanical portions (skeleton, muscles) of an evolving being. Our ever expanding communications network and electronic computer systems are likened to a developing nervous system. In the same chapter Fr. Teilhard shows how the trend towards more leisure time, in which people are able to use their brains because they are freed from the need to labor with their hands, parallels the growth of research, by which mankind becomes more aware. The one trend complements the other as an intrinsic part of noogenesis.

In another chapter, of *The Phenomenon of Man,* he compares the phenomenon of biogenesis with that of noogenesis from a different viewpoint and shows that both exhibit a remarkable unity of structure, unity of mechanism and unity of movement. The unity of structure is apparent because of the 'fannings out' observed in each. For example various political systems, religions, languages, industries, etc. which mankind has evolved over the ages—one originating from another as time passed by—can be likened to the branches on the tree of life. Fr. Teilhard also noted a unity of mechanism because both noogenesis and biogenesis progress by groping and invention, trial and error, survival of the fittest if you like. Finally both noogenesis and biogenesis exhibit the same unity of movement because, and this is most important, both phenomena are moving in the direction of the rise and expansion of consciousness.

> Thus through the combined influence of two curves, both cosmic in nature—one physical (the roundness of the earth) and one psychic (the reflective's self-attraction), mankind is now caught up, as though in a train of gears, at the heart of a continually accelerating vortex of self-totalization.[26]

This is indeed a strange and fantastic idea to those unfamiliar with Fr. Teilhard's far reaching vision. To help people understand it he presented a diagram in several places which I have reproduced in simplified and somewhat modified form in Fig. 2. The lower portion of the diagram representing biogenesis, the 'thought barrier,' and the emergence of man from the primates have already

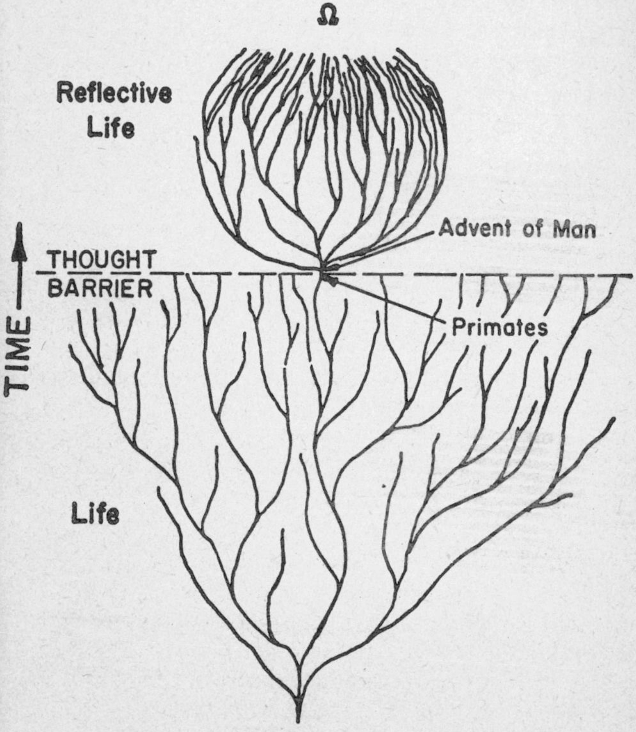

Ω

Reflective Life

Advent of Man

THOUGHT BARRIER

TIME

Primates

Life

FIGURE 2

been discussed. Above the barrier, when life entered a bright new world (reflective life), are shown branchings quite analogous to those which occurred during biogenesis. But there are two important differences between the 'branchings' above the barrier compared to those below it.

The first distinction to be noted is that the branchings above the barrier do *not* represent biological differentiation into different species. Man *is* a species and is becoming more so every day as he intermarries with people of other social strata, religions, ethnic backgrounds and races. The very fact that he is intermarrying is a further indication that mankind is becoming unified—becoming One as Fr. Teilhard would phrase it. Instead, the branchings above the barrier represent the evolution of different kinds of social institutions, using the term 'social institutions' in the broadest sense. In the one and a half million years since man ascended from the apes he has formed, in association with others of his species, an innumerable variety of political and religious systems, civilizations and collectivizations, nationalities, races, etc. Some of these have become extinct (e.g.—ancient Aztec civilization) while others are living and growing on the mental level (e.g.—Christianity). It should be noted that because the diagram represents the evolution *of the society* of Man it is impossible, even in principle, to point to a particular branch and say that one belongs there.

The second and most important distinction to make between 'branchings' in the biosphere and in the noosphere is that, *in the noosphere the branches converge* rather than diverge. This feature is shown clearly on the sketch.

It can be said, rightfully I think, that the sole purpose of Fr. Teilhard's writings was to show man that he, unavoidably, is converging with other men in the dimension of thought. For a long, long time in man's history the convergence was not noticed because the growth of various 'social institutions' had a divergent appearance as man spread over the globe. Nevertheless because man, by his nature, turns inwards upon himself, it was inevitable that the social institutions of which he is a part would sooner or later turn inwards upon themselves and upon one another producing a convergent effect.

Fr. Teilhard likened the upper part of Fig. 2 to an imaginary sphere with two poles; the wave of hominisation proceeding within the sphere from the lower pole (advent of man) to an upper pole, which to avoid prejudicing anyone, he called the Omega point. "Taken over its whole course the wave in question advances in a curved and therefore 'converging' medium: and yet at the same time, during the first half of its passage (as far, that is, as the Equator) it is spreading outwards; beyond that point, however, it begins to contract upon itself." [27] He thought that we had already passed the 'equator' and had entered upon the compressive phase of noogenic evolution. The increasing anxieties, tensions, problems and pressures resulting from the population, pollution, knowledge, communications, transportation, mechanization and other 'explosions' which so intimately affect our lives were the evidence he cited to justify this belief. There was no question in his mind that these tensions would increase. "There is nothing, absolutely nothing—we may as well make up our minds to it—that can arrest the progress of social man towards ever greater interdependence and cohesion." [28]

In another passage the same thought was expressed as follows—"Mankind, born on this planet and spread over its entire surface, is coming gradually to form around its earthly matrix a single major organic unity, enclosed upon itself; a single, hypercomplex, hypercentrated, hyperconscious archmolecule, coextensive with the heavenly body of which it was born." [29] By its use of the words hypercomplex, hypercentrated and hyperconscious this passage emphasizes the idea that what is happening to us today is a logical extension of the law of centrated-complexity—consciousness—but on a global scale. Radial energy is now forcing granules of thought to form some sort of superorganism in which individual men are elements of a 'closed whole' much as it drove atoms to form cells, and cells to form man, in earlier times.

A great many people of course have recognized the forces of socialization which are engulfing us at a seemingly accelerated pace. And most of us, too, are prone to think that collectivization can't possibly continue much more without mechanizing us and minimizing or eliminating our individual freedom and personality. We have only to think of ants in an anthill or bees in a beehive or overcrowded rats in a scientific experiment to conjure up all sorts of pessimistic pictures of what will happen to us when we become compressed much more than we already are. Because most men see the convergence of mankind as a perfectly natural evolutionary process, or, rather, because they see it as *only a natural* phenomenon, they tend to fight it either actively or passively in any way that they can.

But, and this is the big 'but' which Fr. Teilhard tried to make us see, if we look at convergence as *only a natural* phenomenon we are forgetting evolution, we are forgetting that concentration has always in the past led to a higher form of life. He said that rather than compare the socialization of man with the socialization of ants as we did a minute ago we should consider instead the following:

One celled being—evolving to—one cell in a human being

One human being—evolving to—one human being in a planetized mankind

One cell in our bodies, a nerve cell for example, is obviously developed to a much higher extent (has a higher 'personality') and is an integral part of a higher form of life (reflective life) than a one celled organism, a paramecium for example. All it does is swarm around in ponds. It lives but not in the sense that a nerve cell in our bodies lives. True, the nerve cell doesn't have the 'freedom' that a paramecium has to 'go where it wants to and do what it wants to' but the nerve cell participates in a much higher form of freedom, the freedom of man. By extension of the analogy Fr. Teilhard is trying to show us that we will become superpersonalized, superhumanized when we become incorporated into the Omega point. Then we will be truly free.

To further appreciate his reasoning and to show that socialization is not necessarily leading to dehumanization we can use Figure 2 to describe the phenomenon of noogenesis from a slightly different viewpoint. As we did before, visualize a light—this time coinciding with Omega. The analogy is quite good here I believe because Fr. Teilhard believed that Omega truly is the Light of the World, that is, God! Below this light are *three* membranes. One is the membrane I spoke of before which separates life from thought. Another, well below the first and prior to it in time, separates matter from life. The third is immediately below Omega, at the top of the 'sphere' in Fig. 2 representing noogenesis. It is ahead of us in time.

The light which gets through the bottom of the third membrane is extremely diffuse but since it's the only light there is in the cosmos and the cosmos is forced to grow towards the light it moves in that general direction. Finally a breakthrough occurred and (biological) life began when the psychic temperature of matter reached an appropriate level. The next stage has already been described in more detail, viz., life advanced until finally another breakthrough, into the domain of reflective life, occurred. The last stage of which we are a part involves creatures who are evolution become aware of itself. They (we) can perceive Omega whereas no others could. We turn inwards upon ourselves and hence converge—towards Omega because we can see, if we will, that that is where we are going. Fr. Teilhard believed that, at the end of the world, another breakthrough —the final ecstasy of mankind—would occur when mankind reached the epitome of its capabilities, when the psychic temperature of the whole world had reached its ultimate.

We can not visualize what this final 'breakthrough' may be like. We can not comprehend the Incomprehensible. Nevertheless we can perhaps obtain a faint inkling of what it may be like by combining the two previous analogies. An atom obviously doesn't know what it means to live, yet it participates in and is an integral and distinct part of a living cell.—A cell doesn't know what it means to be a man. The idea is incomprehensible to it because it can't think, can't reflect; yet cells when they cooperate with one another ('love' one another and don't fight one another as cancer cells do) are integral and interdependent parts of the 'closed whole' called a man. They too participate in a higher form of life even though individually they can't understand or comprehend the being of which they are a part. In exactly the same way Fr. Teilhard is saying that we are now part of a developing worldwide superorganism in which, *if we love one another,* we can achieve a higher form of life.

The chances are excellent, to put it mildly, that those of us living in the 20th century will not witness the final ecstasy or breakthrough, during our earthly life. The reason is simple. The world isn't ready for it. We still hate. Christ didn't come the first time until the world had evolved to the proper state (i.e., reflective beings on earth as opposed to just dinosaurs for example) and He probably won't come again in Glory until the world has evolved to the proper state, which Fr. Teilhard believed would be when every man truly loved his neighbor, cooperated with him, helped him in any way that he could and therefore loved God—and/or vice versa because you can't truly love your neighbor without loving God.

It is this final feature of Fr. Teilhard's vision which is difficult to understand. It is not surprising because none of us can comprehend the Incomprehensible. Fr. Teilhard's vision therefore is not an airtight proof of the existence of God. Fr. Teilhard did believe however that there is another 'bit' of evidence which supports his theory. (So far I've only alluded to it.) In effect he says that not only is there no valid reason of any kind not to expect that the forces of convergence which we feel will lead to a higher form of life but, in addition, we have positive evidence—from the Incarnation, God became man in the person of Jesus of Nazareth—that we will be superpersonalized and superhumanized in the process of becoming incorporated into *the* Totality, which is the Body of Christ.

That idea is the crux of Fr. Teilhard's vision because he associates the Omega point of evolution with the God of creation, the God of the Old and New Testament, the One God who sent His only begotten Son into the world in the person of Jesus, The Christ. He is the end point of evolution. Although we can't completely understand how, He is He who (That which) is abuilding and being completed by the convergence of Mankind. 'Being completed?' This is not to say that the Triune God is incomplete. Rather I think that Fr. Teilhard means that creation as we see it from our vantage point in our four dimensional space-time is not yet completed. Creation, again—from our perspective in space and in time, wasn't a one-shot job—done and completed. It's a process, still going on in and through us with the indispensable assistance of The Holy Spirit so that 'God may be all in all.' "The world is still being created and in the world it is Christ who is being fulfilled." [30]

Radial energy, which has driven evolution from the beginning, is God's love, His creative Spirit. Towards the end of *The Phenomenon of Man*, Fr. Teilhard has a section entitled 'Love as Energy.' In it and in several other passages he clearly shows (at least so it seems to me) that it is God's love which caused matter to appear in the first place and which is causing the universe to evolve back to Himself. Thus God's love *is* the universe.

We have now closed the circle. We began with the simplest form of matter, without at the time saying where it came from, and have now concluded from a study of evolution that it came from God in the form of energy. And strangely enough, outstanding cosmologists who give no indication of ever having heard of Fr. Teilhard are now beginning to say that before there was matter there was energy!

> Omega, He towards whom all converges, is concurrently He from whom all radiates. Impossible to place him as a focus at the summit of the universe, without at the same time diffusing his presence in the intimate heart of the smallest movement of evolution.[31]

Christogenesis: The Final Phase of Evolution

At this point the reader, hopefully, has a reasonably accurate picture of Fr. Teilhard's vision, but he is probably wondering about Christogenesis—the fourth phase of evolution.

Christogenesis is to Fr. Teilhard the final phase of evolution. In a historic sense we can date its visible origin quite accurately. In fact we date everything with reference to that night in Bethlehem when 'The Word was made flesh and dwelt among us!' Christ is indeed the center of time just as He is the center of everything! But this event, profound though it was, by itself does not really tell us much about the process of Christogenesis as Fr. Teilhard saw it.

Almost every essay of Fr. Teilhard's (other than his strictly scientific papers) and every book written by him emphasizes the thought that *man will not advance unless he sees some outlet, a goal of some sort, ahead of him.* Man, because he knows and knows that he knows, just won't beat his head against a wall, won't continue striving, unless he is convinced that there is something worth striving and even dying for. Since this facet of human nature is so relevant to an understanding of Christogenesis I have selected one rather short statement of Fr. Teilhard's to reinforce the idea.

> What conditions must the universe absolutely fulfill in order that we may be drawn towards ever greater consciousness? This (according to all those who have tried to discover the psychological mechanism of action) is the condition: that we shall not imagine the movement that beckons us forward to be condemned in advance to stop or draw back. We must know that it is, by nature, *irreversible.* Promise man as many millions of years as you will. Let him glimpse at the end of that period as high (that is to say as superhuman) a summit as you will. If it is known beforehand that, once that summit is reached, we shall have to descend without any signs of our ascent surviving in the universe; then, I say plainly, we shall not have the heart to advance, and we shall not advance. Whatever Jeans and Langevin may say man will never consent to labor like a Sisyphus.[32]

There is an even more fundamental idea underlying the previous one which forms the kernel of Fr. Teilhard's vision. The 'outlet' which man must see in front of him if he's going to continue to live, individually and/or collectively, can not be an 'it' or an 'idea'; it must be a person because man can never be completely fulfilled except in, with and through another person.

> An *irreversible* rise towards the *personal:* unless it satisfies some Whole comprising these two conjoined attributes, the Universe (psychoanalytically dosed, if I may put it that way) can only become stifling for all reflective activity, that is to

> say, radically unsuited to any rebound of Evolution. But we are agreed that such a rebound is preparing and indeed has already begun. So we must conclude, unless we favor the idea of a world destined to miscarry through a fault in its construction, that evolutionary irreversibility and personalisation (despite their implied anticipation of the future) are realities not of a *metaphysical* but of a physical order, in the sense that, like the dimensions of Time and Space, they represent general conditions to which the totality of our proceedings must conform.[33]

Another expression of this idea which will be particularly meaningful to the existentialists is the following:

> A veritable *Ego* at the summit of the world is needed for the consummation, without confounding them, of all the elemental *egos* of Earth. . . . I have talked of the 'Christian View,' but this idea is gaining ground in other circles. Was it not Camus who wrote in Sisyphe, 'If Man found that the Universe could love he would be reconciled?' And did not Wells, through his exponent the humanitarian biologist Steele in *The Anatomy of Frustration*, express his need to find, above and beyond humanity a 'universal lover?' [34]

The dream of a utopia, of universal brotherly love, peace on earth, and goodwill to all is common to almost all men regardless of their formal religious affiliation or beliefs. Fr. Teilhard was sympathetic to all movements of this type and believed that each was in fact contributing, in its own unique and invaluable way, towards this goal to which we all aspire. But he also believed that it would be impossible to achieve this state of 'heaven' on earth without help from above, as it were. The great fallacy he saw in all purely human or natural efforts towards unity (socialism as commonly understood, for example, or natural humanism) is that they were destined to fail because they do not definitely eliminate death. They are built upon the earth and will vanish with the earth. They do not incorporate the supernatural element and therefore can never provide an answer to the ultimate question reflective man asks himself about death. From reasoning like this Fr. Teilhard believed sooner or later, all mankind would truly recognize that the only possible salvation was in Christ.

What he was trying to show us is that when enough people develop an evolutionary perspective and understand God's plan more completely then the trend towards unity among mankind will be achieved *willingly* through attraction towards a common objective—Christ Omega. When mankind finally realizes that petty self-aggrandisement, racial strife, religious antagonisms, political hatred, nationalistic wars and all other forms of 'wasted tangential' (viz.—non-Christ centered) activity serve no purpose other than delaying the inevitable then we will become truly united in one ultrahuman, superpersonal, hypercomplex body—The Body of Christ.

Christogenesis will supercede noogenesis when the push from behind, so to speak, is supplanted by the pull from up front—that is when every man is overpowered in everything he does by his love for God. And God, returning this love in the form of an ever-increasing flux of grace (radial energy) to His universe, will then complete the act of creation. Mankind will then undergo the final act of consummation.

Fr. Teilhard was not a professional theologian. Partly for this reason undoubtedly and partly because his main mission in life was to fight modern man's tendency to despair, escapism and pessimism in a language and idiom attuned to the times, his theology and Christology are considered to be rather one-sided by professional theologians. This is not to say that his ideas are totally, or even partially, in error from a theological viewpoint but they are open to suspicion and misunderstanding. Fr. Christopher Mooney has put these problems in proper perspective and in a very lucid paragraph has explained how the person of Christ *necessarily must be* an essential element in the evolutionary scheme of things as envisioned by Fr. Teilhard. Here is how he phrased it.

> The ultimate guarantee of evolution's success has to be Christ's victory over sin, for without such a victory the relationship between Christ and the universe, that is to say, the whole positive aspect of redemption, can neither be safeguarded nor even correctly understood. There can be no growth in spirit from deficiency of matter except in so far as the love of Christ fosters love among men. And for this to take place there must first be a healing of that 'disconcerting excess' in man's rejection of love, the sole source of which is the reparation made by Christ for the sins of the world.[35]

Summary of Fr. Teilhard's Vision

To help people see how logically and consistently his 'theory' harmonizes with the 'facts,' Fr. Teilhard likened the evolutionary process, particularly since the advent of man, to a cone; the axis of the cone represents the axis of evolution. Evolution proceeds in a converging sense towards the apex of the cone, the Omega point.

With this analogy before us let us review all of the preceding arguments in our mind. Since the Omega point is the focus towards which all of evolution has been directed, from the beginning to the end, it can be characterized by the term *existence* or *actuality*. Beneath the surface, evolution exhibits a unity involving everything. Omega, can therefore be described by the words *unity* and *totality*. Evolution has progressed always in the direction of higher forms of life and is irreversible. Therefore Omega is *supremely aware* and *immortal*. Omega must exist independently of matter and man in order to satisfy the ultimate requirements of our action. Therefore Omega is also *autonomous*. In addition we can deduce that the Omega point must be *transcendent* because "if by it's very nature it did not escape from the time and space which it gathers together, it would not be Omega." [36] But this is not all. The most important feature of Fr. Teilhard's vision will be missed completely if we fail to realize that Omega, which is God, must of necessity be a *Personal God*. Since the convergent point of evolution is a convergence point of persons raised to ever-increasing heights of awareness and personality, then the Omega point must be a *Supreme Person*. Paraphrased slightly, here is how Fr. Teilhard puts it. "A world conceived as drifting towards the Impersonal . . . would become at once unthinkable and unlivable, for from such a world we could draw neither the warmth of attraction nor the hope of irreversibility (immortality) without which our own selfishness will always have the last world." [37]

Existence, Actuality, Unity, Totality, Immortality, Supremely Aware, Autonomy, Transcendence, Personal, Supreme Person—These are some of the attributes of Omega which follow from Fr. Teilhard's vision of evolution. Fr. Teilhard never said, however, that they define God, or exhaust His attributes, because He is *Undefinable, Inexhaustible* and *Incomprehensible* in His totality.

Because it incorporates a supernatural element, there are many who can not accept Fr. Teilhard's vision of reality. For them especially he wrote the following.

> Clearly this is a matter in which I cannot compel your assent. But I can assure you, of my own experience, that the acceptance of this organic and realistic view of the social phenomenon is both eminently satisfying to our reason and fortifying to our will.
>
> Satisfying to our intelligence above all. For if it be true that at this moment Mankind is embarking upon what I have called its 'phase of planetization,' then everything is clarified, everything in our field of vision acquires a new sharpness of outline.
>
> The tightening network of economic and psychic bonds in which we live and from which we suffer, the growing compulsion to act, to produce, to think collectively which so disquiets us—what do they become, seen in this way except for the first portents of the super-organism which, woven of the threads of individual men, is preparing (theory and fact are at one on this point) not to mechanize and submerge us, but to raise us, by way of increasing complexity, to a higher awareness of our own personality? . . .
>
> And, let it be added, *sustenance and necessary reassurance for our power of will.* Through the centuries life has become an increasingly heavy burden for Man the Species, just as it does for Man the Individual as the years pass. The modern world, with its prodigious growth of complexity, weighs incomparably more heavily upon the shoulders of our generation than did the ancient world upon the shoulders of our forebears. Have you never felt that this added load needs to be

> compensated for by an added passion, a new sense of purpose? To my mind, this is what is 'providently' arising to sustian our courage—the hope, the belief that some immense fulfillment lies ahead of us.[38]

* * * * * *

I think that many features of Fr. Teilhard's vision can be summarized by an abstract drawing which is at the same time a sort of scientific schematic diagram, Figure 3. I call this drawing 'The Divine Milieu' after Fr. Teilhard's book of the same name.

The focal point is obviously the Omega point—but the whole drawing is supposed to represent God. He is everywhere, not just at the center. He permeates and activates everything that ever was or ever will be. He is immanent. But Fr. Teilhard's theory is not pantheism because God is simultaneously at the center of everything and is a personal God.

Emanating from the Omega point are radiations which diverge. They soon become diffuse as at the periphery of the sketch. Cosmogenesis can be thought of as the region where the radial lines, representing radial energy, are diffuse. Here the 'without' of creation is most apparent. But still there is a tendency for the universe to go back to Omega and the cosmos begins to turn back when life appears in the universe (biogenesis). The tendency to concentrate becomes greatei and a definite cone of convergence begins to take shape (near the bottom) with the advent of noogenesis in man. The 'within' now begins to predominate. From then on the cone of life converges more rapidly and ultimately returns to God. Notice that it returns upward to God, ever upwards to higher forms of life.

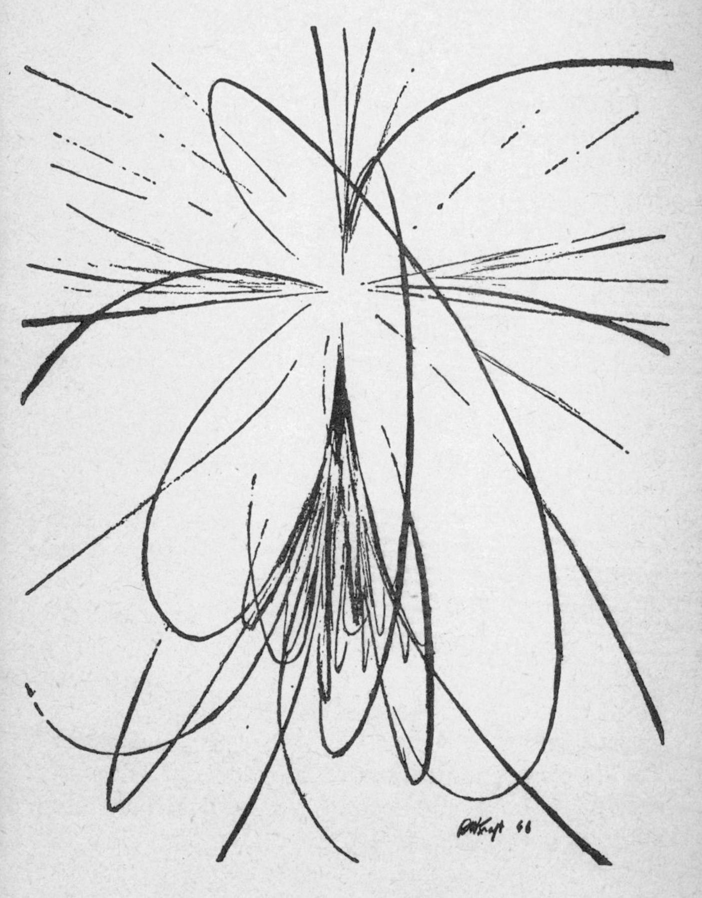

FIGURE 3

The radial lines just described as representing radial energy really signify God's love. In other words it is God's love for His creation which is the fundamental driving force which causes matter to appear and makes the universe evolve into more complex, then more aware, and finally more spiritual 'things.' In fact, in a sense, God's love *is* the universe. But God's love is not just a driving force which compels. It is also an attractive force which inspires man to strive for the impossible!

The axis of evolution can be thought of as one of the lines going through the cone. It begins in the dim past at God, progresses through the various stages of evolution and terminates again in God. If we imagine our four-dimensional space-time reduced to one of these one-dimensional lines it could represent an evolutionary time scale. The present can be thought of as a point on this line within the cone of convergence. The future would then be represented by points farther up along the line within the cone (i.e., towards Omega) and the past by points farther back along the line in the region where the radial lines are farther apart (viz. God's love less apparent). Like many mathematical functions in the vicinity of a critical point (viz., tangent of an angle between 89° and 91°) we see that plus infinity merges imperceptibly with minus infinity at the Omega point. The incomprehensible infinities of space and time are merged at Omega. The Omega point of our evolutionary time scale is simultaneously the Alpha point. God is the beginning and the end, the foundation stone and the keystone.

In addition, since God is represented by all the lines on the diagram and not just by the one line representing our evolution, He is above and outside and apart from our time and space. He transcends everything we can visualize.

Slightly below Omega on the cone of convergence representing noogenesis I've shown a point or spark from which, as one moves his eye upwards towards Omega, the cone becomes more intensely shaded (i.e., society's psychic temperature increases). As the drift of evolution proceeds upwards towards Omega this shading gradually consumes the whole cone. The spark (originating from a radial line emanating directly from Omega—as indeed all radial lines do) represents the Incarnation whereby God made his plan known to men. The ever more intensely shaded, ever tightening and converging cone represents Christogenesis, the culmination of noogenesis, when more and more men finally realize their destiny and act in a spirit of genuine love—towards each other and towards God.

The end of the world will come when it has evolved to the proper state. Then Christ will come again and God will complete His act of creation—an act which has been in progress from the beginning. This does not mean, nor does Fr. Teilhard say, that man can think his way to God for faith in God is a gift from Him. When God wills it there will be a final transition, a final ecstasy, for us as individuals when we die and for the world at the end of time, which we cannot conceive but which we know, from the Bible, will be wonderful and something to be desired for those whose fundamental attitude is God-directed. Fr. Teilhard's vision certainly shows us that the Parousia will only be achieved when we all focus our lives on Christ in *everything* that we do.

Without being too obvious (because I didn't want to detract from the other ideas this sketch suggests) I've shown the radiations emanating from Omega in slightly more pronounced form in the horizontal and vertical directions. This array of horizontal and vertical lines suggests a cross indicating that God is a personal God who came down to earth to save us and lead us back to Himself. The cross is centered on Omega. Christ is coincident with God; both are represented by the whole drawing. Christ is the central feature of Fr. Teilhard's vision and He is central to our universe.

The Trinity can be thought of as follows. The Father is the *whole drawing*. The Son is the *array* of radial lines in the form of a cross. The Holy Spirit is represented by the radial *lines* which signify radial energy or love or life giving spirit. The *whole drawing* is the *array of lines* which in turn consists of *the lines themselves*. The Three Persons are somehow different aspects of God yet they are one and the same—Three Persons in one Nature.

Finally, imagine that the drawing, instead of being reproduced on paper or canvas, was painted on a mirror. The mirror itself (before the lines were drawn) was of variable reflectivity; it produced a hazy image near the periphery, like an old mirror which had lost some of its silver, but was perfect at that point at which the Omega point was subsequently imposed by the paint in the lines of the drawing. . . Room light reflected from this drawing-on-a-mirror will be most intensely reflected from the Omega point, suggesting the idea that God is the Light of the Cosmos.

The drawing-on-a-mirror still represents creation. As I look squarely at it I see myself in relation to all of creation. I see that I am a unique creature for the simple reason that no one else can produce the image *I* see as I look at the mirror. Although my vision is obscured I notice as I look at the drawing that everything is clearest when I focus on Omega. I also see Christ (the cross) in me and me in Christ. And as I stand aside to let my neighbor look into the drawing-on-the-mirror I see his image where mine just was. If I look carefully I can see Christ in him too.

* * * * * *

> God does not offer Himself to our finite beings as a thing all complete and ready to be embraced. For us He is eternal discovery and eternal growth. The more we think we understand Him, the more He reveals Himself as otherwise. The more we think we hold Him, the further He withdraws, drawing us into the depths of Himself. The nearer we approach Him through all the efforts of nature and grace, the more He increases, in one and the same movement, His attraction over our powers, and the receptivity of our powers to that divine attraction.[39]

ITS RELEVANCE

Albert Einstein once wrote: "A theory is the more impressive the greater the simplicity of its premises is, the more different kinds of things it relates, and the more extended is its area of applicability." With this dictum in mind it seems worthwhile to reflect for a moment upon Fr. Teilhard's theory as described in the previous chapter and upon his definition of truth.

> *Truth* is simply the complete coherence of the universe in relation to every point contained within it. Why should we be suspicious of or underestimate this coherence just because we ourselves are the observers? We hear continually of some sort of anthropocentric illusion contrasted with some sort of objective reality. In fact, there is no such distinction. Man's truth is the truth of the universe for man; in other words it is simply truth.[40]

Each reader of this book must decide for himself whether he thinks Fr. Teilhard's theory is 'the truth of the universe for man,' now, as well as he can understand it,—or whether he thinks it is merely a meaningless or exaggerated hypothesis, or an illusion, or pseudoscience tied together with poetical mysticism. I believe it is the former and it is from such a viewpoint that this chapter is written.

As several commentators have pointed out his vision is so vast that it runs the risk of remaining exclusively on the level of God's total plan and therefore of being irrelevant on the level of immediate human experience. The problems of earning a living, raising families, and trying to preserve human values in a war torn world and in a society which seems to be smothering us with anonymity don't appear to be solvable by some grandoise theory which assures us that things will probably work out for the better, eventually. Most of us want to have things get better sooner than that, to see and make some visible progress and to obtain some satisfaction for our efforts.

Fr. Teilhard believed that most men would eventually learn to work with the evolutionary tide and not against it, as so many of us do. That is why he was fundamentally an optimist. But his main point was: —Why wait for eventually? Since we can see what is happening to the world why on earth don't we get to work right now and help it along, every one of us? We *do* have it in our power to change the world and make it a better place in which to live, we *can* help in building heaven for the simple reason that we are evolution become aware of itself, we *must* do this lest we perish.

The beauty of this attitude, this faith, this approach to life is that once we decide to adopt it we develop a passion for building the earth according to God's plan. We learn to treasure the only goal of ultimate value and to put all intermediate goals in their proper place in the scheme of things. We learn how to choose worthwhile intermediate goals and how to forget them once they are achieved without being consumed by them.

We begin to see why and how each one of us is of inestimable value, and simultaneously insignificant in relation to God. We learn to become more tolerant, to accept other people for what they are because we appreciate that every person, by virtue of his existence, contributes to the universe something unique. We learn to be patient because we realize that no one escapes the evolutionary process, which at times seems to us to be proceeding too slowly—or too rapidly. Simultaneously we become impatient because we yearn for the peace, justice and charity associated with the only reality that is unchanging.

We learn that peace is not the absence of war

or the 'good life' in a crass materialistic sense but a continual struggle—for Something which is always better. The meaning of genuine earthly progress, which is most compatible with spiritual progress towards Omega, becomes clearer as do rightful means for making progress. We learn that true progress will only be made when we, as individuals, by acts of our free will, make the decision to promote the only kind of order and unity capable of withstanding the vicissitudes of space and time and capable of sustaining our will to progress. And when we have learned all this we learn that true peace will only be achieved when every man learns that he is his brother's keeper—*and acts accordingly.*

We realize that the only truly complete satisfaction for our appetites and desires lies in He who is truth, knowledge, energy, love—in short in He who is. The frustrations and sufferings which we undergo then take on a completely different meaning.

And finally, we realize how helpless we are without God's grace and we learn to have hope, without which we are lost before we begin.

* * * * * *

To help us develop this attitude of love, this belief in progress, this faith in the future Fr. Teilhard placed great emphasis on the verb seeing.

Seeing

> Seeing. We might say that the whole of life lies in that verb—if not ultimately, at least essentially. Fuller being is closer union: such is the kernel and conclusion of this book (The Phenomenon of Man). But let us emphasize the point: union in-

> creases only through an increase in consciousness, that is to say in vision. And that, doubtless, is why the history of the living world can be summarized as the elaboration of ever more perfect eyes within a cosmos in which there is always something to be seen. After all, do we not judge the perfection of an animal, or the supremacy of a thinking being, by the penetration and synthetic power of their gaze. To try to see more and better is not a matter of whim or curiosity or self-indulgence. *To see or to perish* is the very condition laid upon everything that makes up the universe, by reason of the mysterious gift of existence. And this, in superior measure, is man's condition.[41]

Fr. Teilhard was trying to teach us to look at the world around us—the earth and it's plant and animal life, man and his activities and social institutions, space and time—as a whole. He was trying to show us that the only proper way to envision any one phenomenon, object, being, idea or institution is in relation to the totality of everything. With his remarkable ability to do this he was able to see the unity in God's creation and to deduce what he believed to be the underlying process of which everything is a part.

Most of us, however, have difficulty in seeing things this way. We suffer from a defective vision, which commonly takes one of two forms. The first is a tendency towards 'compartmentalized' vision, the second a tendency towards 'shortsightedness.' One might say the former is a spatial defect whereas the latter is a temporal defect. By compartmentalization I mean the tendency to see everything good or bad, etc. By shortsightedness I mean the lack of an evolutionary perspective, the inability to see beyond our own small worlds and short lives. Let us examine how each of these defects in vision influences our thinking.

First is compartmentalization. Because of our tendency to compartmentalize everything we see, we tend to think that anything and everything can be neatly categorized and isolated from everything else. In business we see only the balance sheet. Thus we tend to think exclusively in terms of profit and loss and forget that human values can not be measured in terms of dollars and cents. In engineering and science we arbitrarily establish interfaces between the system and the environment and then proceed to solve, or at least try to solve, the technological problems of the system—all too frequently forgetting the initial and arbitrary boundary conditions under which any solution we might obtain is valid. In politics we create boundaries between towns, states, and countries and then oftentimes selfishly neglect to consider the effects of our votes, legislative actions and policies on those who live in another town, state or country. In the field of international relations our tendency is to see only the differences between capitalism and communism. Depending on our political beliefs we condemn one and extol the virtues of the other meanwhile forgetting that in each there are elements of value and some not-so-desirable features.

It is the same in all fields of human endeavor. With our compartmentalized vision we tend to emphasize the apparent dichotomies between science and religion, labor and management, theism and humanism, theory and practice, the discrete and the continuous, the secular and the sacred, the black and the white races, oriental and occidental, progressives and conservatives, urban and suburban. . . . The list is endless.

The danger in seeing things this way is that it

leads us to think that it is possible to isolate one regime from another. But this of course is impossible because everything in the universe is related in some way to everything else. Not only this, but in so viewing things we tend to forget that the total is greater than the sum of its parts. A man is more than a highly complex arrangement of cells; a home is more than bricks, lumber and appliances; a government is more than a collection of laws, leaders and legislatures; a university is more than faculty, students, buildings and books. . . . Unless we try to overcome compartmentalized vision it will be difficult, if not impossible, for us to see the interrelationship, the unity, the order among everything in the universe.

Closely akin to compartmentalization is shortsightedness. In compartmentalizing ideas, institutions, systems, things and processes we also tend to forget time. Because we are finite creatures with only a brief life span allotted to us on earth we have difficulty in seeing the world from an evolutionary perspective. This frequently leads to one of two diametrically opposite views of time, both of which are equally erroneous as are most black or white pictures of the world.

At one extreme are those who are impatient to change the world during their lifetimes. These are the revolutionaries of all kinds who want instant reforms. Time is passing too slowly for them: they forget that evolution is a process which follows God's plan, not theirs. They forget that we were created in time but not for time, and therefore that nothing in time will ever completely satisfy anyone. Although they are correct when they realize that man can accelerate evolution they frequently do not see the whole picture (because of a 'spatial' defect in vision) and consequently retard true progress by their actions.

At the other extreme are those who can not or will not see that the world *is* changing. This outlook is perhaps not as prevalent today as it was a generation ago because the changes which are occurring in society, politics, technology, etc. are influencing us so drastically and at such a seemingly accelerating rate that we can't help but notice them. Still there is a tendency on the part of some to try to slow down time, to repress progress because of a fear of what the future holds. Time passes too quickly for advocates of the status quo. They do not want their government, their church, their company, their neighborhood to change and they therefore resist the forces of socialization, religious renewal, new ideas, racial integration—changes in general. Although they are correct when they realize that order must be maintained they frequently do not see that true progress is only made through the efforts of man to make a better world; and this requires change. The fact is that without change there wouldn't be any time and there wouldn't be any life. No time because time has meaning only in the context of change. No life because without change there is no growth. Time, life and growth in awareness are all inextricably entwined in the evolutionary process.

Fr. Teilhard tried to show us that 'compartmentalized vision' and 'shortsightedness' can be deadly because in so viewing the world and the human situation we're not looking at the *whole* problem, which is that of building the earth for Christ. The danger in chopping this whole problem up to solve piecemeal lies in the fact that, in so doing, we frequently ignore or forget facets of the whole problem which lie 'outside' the little piece we have chosen to attack. Invariably however any solution to a piece of the total problem, sooner or later, has repercussions outside the initial and arbitrary boundaries of the piece. These repercussions have a tendency to snowball and compound our difficulties as the world becomes smaller and more complex.

What we must try to do, Fr. Teilhard urges us, is to develop a unified view of the world and an evolutionary perspective. Then we will be able to see more clearly that all the arbitrary boundaries that have been established over the ages are gradually disappearing with the passage of time as mankind converges upon itself and upon Omega.

It would be superfluous at this point to add more examples illustrating the convergence of mankind. All one has to do is read almost any newspaper, magazine or book or just open his eyes and look at the world to realize that we are becoming more interdependent and simultaneously more aware with each passing day. Beneath the growth pains of a world entering a new era we are, to borrow some terms from Marshall McLuhan, a growing 'global village' under the influence of 'electric media' (telephone, radio, TV, computers, automation, satellites, etc.). Needless to say Fr. Teilhard is not the only one who is teaching us these facts of life, although he is, in my opinion, the only one who has shown us how to see *beyond* the obvious so clearly. The progressive infolding of mankind upon itself is, it seems to me, a sociological fact beyond dispute, as are its effects—namely that we are converging in the domain of reflective conciousness on Christ-Omega, the source of our faith in the future and our goal.

The primary value of Fr. Teilhard's vision lies in showing those of us who can see it how "All things have been created through and unto him, and (how) he is before all creatures, and (how) in him all things hold together."[42] This is not to imply that Fr. Teilhard has once and for all times completely answered all the 'how' and 'why' questions that man can ask or that he has 'explained' Christ. But he has shown us how to see order and unity in the universe. The evolutionary law of increasing complexity-consciousness provides the means to do this. The source of this law, God's love, which manifests itself at the earlier stages of evolution as radial energy, naturally leads us to Christ. His theory thus incorporates space and time, man and society, matter and spirit in one unified vision. For these reasons it is intellectually satisfying, immensely consoling and inspiring, and above all religiously meaningful to those of us who can see it. Furthermore it is timeless because its central feature is Christ who transcends time.

Due to differences in education, outlook on life, temperament and any number of other personality traits, not everyone is disposed to see things in the way that Fr. Teilhard did. As Fr. Raymond Nogar expressed it in *The Lord of the Absurd* when referring to Fr. Teilhard's work "The universe may, in point of fact, *be one;* when God looks upon the universe He may *see it to be one;* but when I look out upon the universe of matter, of man and of God's handiwork, *I do not see it as one.*" Of course the fact that some people are unable to view the world through Fr. Teilhard's eyes in no way invalidates his 'theory,' as Fr. Nogar emphasizes. But whether or not we see the world as he did, whether or not we believe his theory as a theory, is not the important point.

What is crucial is whether or not we see God who IS Lord of the Absurd as well as Lord of Order, whether or not we believe in Him, and *how we act.*

Acting

> One could well say that today, as was the case in Galilee, what we most need if we are to recognize the convergence of the universe is not so much new facts (there are enough, and even embarrassingly more than enough, of these everywhere) as a new way of looking at and handling facts. A new way of seeing, combined with a new way of acting: that is what we need. . . . What we have to do is make up our minds and get to work—*quickly, right now.*[43]

God's love, which caused matter to appear, which made the universe evolve into more complex molecules and then more aware animals, is now forcing us humans to converge on Omega so that we will become more spiritual. If only we could see that, we would realize that the best rule for every one of our free actions is to respond to God's love. Then we would be moving, individually and collectively, with the evolutionary tide, not against it. And how do we return God's love? By loving our neighbor as Christ taught us to do. That in sum and substance is Fr. Teilhard's message.

And the most significant part of it, the most important 'detail' as it was described earlier, is the rule for action.

Building the earth, for Christ, so that God may be all in all is why we are here. Hence our rule for action is to love God, through Christ, in our neighbor. As we build the earth for Him we incidentally make a better world for ourselves. What more beautiful, and terrifying, rule can be imagined? Even the simplest, least educated and unsophisticated person helps build the earth when he loves God and his neighbor. And the arrogant, selfish, complacent and unconcerned individual is adding his share of destruction to the world as well as to himself when he ignores the plight of his neighbor.

* * * * * *

> 'Love one another, recognizing in the heart of each one of you the same God who is being born.' Those words, first spoken two thousand years ago, now begin to reveal themselves as the essential structural law of what we might call progress and evolution.[44]

The primary and overriding feature of Fr. Teilhard's rule for action is to love one's neighbor as Christ taught us to do. We must try to do this even if our neighbor has a differently colored skin, even if he belongs to a political party or religion with which we don't agree, even if we disapprove of his tactics or think he is evil. By passages such as this one Fr. Teilhard was trying to show us that the most important 'things' in the world are persons. Each one of them is infinitely more valuable than anything else imaginable—save God, who is a conserver of persons, as Fr. Teilhard put it. He tried to show us that we are all part of a developing 'closed whole' in which each individual person has a unique role to play. Just as in our bodies each cell has a different appearance and a different function, so each person contributes something uniquely his own to an evolving mankind. We must try to recognize this and value it because it is each person's contribution to *the* Totality of everything, because the universe *is* One.

There will be many who will say this rule is impractical, unworkable, impossible to follow; we can't base the hard decisions of business, government, etc. on love because if we do, our business or our government won't survive. Fr. Teilhard's answers to some of these practical problems are given in the quotations which follow. Nevertheless, were he still alive, I am sure he would say that each one of us should take a good hard look at our sense of values and ask ourselves the question: What am I putting first in my life–God or something else? If we put Him first then inevitably we will be helping to build the earth through our actions but if we put ourselves or wealth or power or fame first then we are in trouble, whether we realize it or not.

Of course there are those who do not believe in a transcendent God. Not infrequently they say 'God' is a meaningless concept because His presence or existence is not verifiable. But God does mean something to those who believe in Him and His presence is manifested–by the actions of those who believe in Him. God *does* make a difference–the difference between hope and despair, freedom and slavery, life and death. His effects on man *are* revealed in their attitudes and actions which can be either generous or greedy, selfless or selfish, loving or hateful, considerate or inconsiderate, compassionate or hard-hearted.

So the answer to the assertion that God is not knowable is that He can be known through the actions of those who believe in Him. The pity is that so many who claim to believe in Him do not act as though they do–but this is due to the sin of man, not to the death or inexistence of God. (Sin, evil and hell have thus far not been mentioned in this book. These negative subjects are treated briefly in Appendix II.)

No one, of course, can ever fully grasp the mystery of God—at least not while he is living on earth—but this does not mean that He is completely hidden from us. He *does* reveal Himself to us, progressively, in time: that is the story of the Bible and the story of evolution. If we want to hear and see Him, we, *by an action of our free will,* must decide to listen to Him and/or look at creation with the attitude that it is, or at least could be, His handiwork. . . . "God is a very simple choice, the choice between a Yes and a No, between a plus sign and a minus sign. This is the choice that none of us can escape."[45]

* * * * * *

> God's creative power does not in fact fashion us as though of soft clay: it is a fire that kindles life in whatever it touches, a quickening spirit. Therefore it is *during our lifetime* that we must decisively adapt ourselves to it, identify ourselves with it. The mystic is given at times a keen, obsessive insight into this situation. And anyone who has this insight, and who loves, will feel within himself a fever of active dependence and of arduous purity seizing upon him and driving him on to an absolute integrity and the complete utilization of all his powers.
>
> In order to become perfectly resonant to the pulsations of the basic rhythm of reality the mystic makes himself docile to the least hint of human obligation, the most unobtrusive demands of grace.
>
> To win for himself a little more of the creative energy, he tirelessly develops his thought, dilates

> his heart, intensifies his external activity. For created beings must work if they would be yet further created.[46]
>
> We who are Christ's disciples must not hesitate to harness this force—the world's expectancy and ferment and unfolding—which needs us and which we need. On the contrary, under pain of allowing it to be dissipated and of perishing ourselves, we must share in those aspirations, in essence authentically religious, which make men today so intensely aware of the immensity of the world, the grandeur of the mind and the sacred value of every newly discovered truth. This is the schooling which will teach our present Christian generation how to await the future.[47]

Love for God and our neighbor is the key element in building the earth for Christ. But as these passages fairly shout and as most major religious bodies today emphasize, pious platitudes and good intentions are not enough. In whatever vocation we find ourselves what we must do is work, expend ourselves, develop our talents to the fullest, learn and do as much as we can—all for the benefit of others. The intrinsic value of human effort, the results of which we call progress, is what Fr. Teilhard had in mind by the word 'forward' when he wrote that the universe is centrated evolutively upward and forward (see item 3 of his summary on page 36).

* * * * * *

> To keep up a constant pressure on the surface of the real, is not that the supreme gesture of faith in Being and therefore the highest form of adoration?
>
> All that is ours, if we understand how to avoid stifling within us the Spirit of Earth.
>
> Whoever wishes to be part of this Spirit must

> die and be born again, for others and for himself.
>
> In order to reach this higher plane of humanity he must bring about a complete transformation in his whole sense of values and his whole action.[48]

These few lines of prose poetry, some of the most beautiful ever written, are part of an essay entitled *The Spirit of Earth* in which Fr. Teilhard tried to show us that love, human unity and research (whereby man increases his awareness of the universe) are the keys to true progress. The particular passage cited formed part of the section dealing with research; it expresses his belief that we must always strive to learn more about nature so that we can learn to control it for the benefit of man.

However I think the quotation can be applied equally well to all human activity. We must keep up a *constant* pressure on the real problems of the world—poverty, starvation, injustice, ignorance—and not become discouraged, or rebellious, when we find that the problems are not solved instantaneously. If we are tolerant of others yet never cease trying to make a better world then we will be building the earth for Christ. It's as simple as that.

* * * * * *

> Under all circumstances always advance upwards, where technically, mentally and affectively everything (in us and around us) *most rapidly converges*. Truly an infallible rule, since by virtue of a curve inherent in the universe we cannot follow it without drawing nearer (even in the thickest darkness) to some supreme and saving pole of super-consciousness.[49]

Since Fr. Teilhard's vision encompasses everything, it is relevant to everything—every phenomenon, every person, every action and every decision. As the reader will surely realize by now Fr. Teilhard believed that every one of our free actions means something—for better or worse. Yet he realized that it is oftentimes difficult to determine whether a given decision is right or wrong. The expression of his rule for action given above is one of the most practical in the sense that it provides a criterion for judging whether a given action or a particular decision which we make is 'for' or 'against' evolution.

To give some down-to-earth examples illustrating how this rule for action (which, let it be reiterated, is nothing more than a modern paraphrasing of Christ's teachings) can be applied, I have chosen the area of race relations in the United States. Neither the nature of this problem nor the urgent need for finding a satisfactory solution require discussion here but I think it would be worthwhile to show how I believe the above rule can and should be applied to a few aspects of this specific problem.

—The doctrine of 'separate but equal' is wrong because 'separate' leads to divergence, not convergence, of the races.

—The doctrines of 'black power' or 'white power' (interpreted militantly and aggressively) are wrong because both are basically nothing more than collective selfishness which inevitably leads to divergence.

—Any attempt—overt or covert, active or passive, blunt or subtle—to prevent negroes from living in white neighborhoods is wrong for the same reason. In fact if we apply Fr. Teilhard's rule for action (and Christian teaching) in a positive sense, as we should, rather than negatively we conclude that all of us should be working to promote fair housing laws and de facto fair housing. (Is not the fact that our country is slowly but surely moving in this direction further proof that Fr. Teilhard's interpretation of evolution and the Christian message is valid?)

I consider the convergence rule cited immediately above to be an excellent value scale which is most useful on a day-to-day decision-by-decision basis. It proscribes a value system which, with a little reflection, can be used anywhere, under all conditions. It incorporates the idea of love (convergence), directed action (under all circumstances always advance), and is applicable in all domains of human activity (technical, mental and affective). Because the ultimate of goodness on this value scale is 'good' spelled with one less 'o' it is a much better value scale than, say, money—unless one happens to believe that an infinite number of dollars is heaven.

It is tempting to give many more examples of the application of this rule in the areas of daily life, business, scientific research, international relations and so forth ad infinitum. But since at our present stage of evolution there is not unanimity and because each person must apply the rule as he sees it (to remain true to himself as Fr. Teilhard urged us to do) we will pass on to another element in Fr. Teilhard's 'rule for action.'

* * * * * *

It is not everything to have located the peak to be climbed. We still have to climb it. . . . Once

> we have recognized and made up our minds that races and nations must unite, the choice of the route to follow and the question of the methods to be employed still confront us. These are infinitely complex technical problems . . . Of course, whatever the circumstances, we cannot answer these manifold questions except by following the method universally applied by life from its beginnings: a slow and patient exploration.[50]

In addition to love and directed action Fr. Teilhard preached, and lived, patience. Progress since the beginning, whenever that was, has always and only been made by the evolutionary process of trial and error. So even though we humans are evolution become aware of itself (and therefore can accelerate evolution by our actions, and must do so in order to build the world for Christ) we have not escaped the evolutionary process. We can not expect God to change His modus operandi just because we are becoming more aware of it or make Him terminate the process, because the end (ours and the worlds) will only come when He wills it. Therefore we must resign ourselves to finding the best way to solve practical problems by a slow and patient exploration.

I think that in general we citizens of the so-called advanced nations would be more patient, would lead happier lives and not be so frustrated by the clock and the calendar if we would take more time to be human. This is something of value we members of the 'highly developed' countries can learn from some of the 'backward' peoples of the world. After all, why do we rush around so much? What is time? The only reason we fret about it is because we're impatient. If we're honest with ourselves, deep down, aren't we impatient most of the time because *we want the satisfaction* of seeing something accomplished? If our ultimate goal in life is to satisfy *ourselves* then this is self-love which is antithetical to loving God.

This does not mean that we should sit back, be apathetic to the plight of our neighbor, and permit the forces of divergence to destroy the world. Far from it. We must continually strive to find a better way to reach our ultimate goal, by non-violent action directed towards this goal.

In my opinion Dr. Martin Luther King exemplified the proper attitude and action for us to take in seeking a better way to avoid and/or correct evolutionary 'errors'. There was no question in Dr. King's mind, nor in Fr. Teilhard's, that the Christian way is the best way to solve our problems. But the specific details of how Christianity is put into practice, in time, can only be worked out by a process of trial and error by compassionate and patient men like them who keep up a constant pressure on the surface of the real without becoming rebellious.

In this connection it is interesting to note that Fr. Teilhard believed that the 'axis of life passed through Rome;' hence his undying loyalty to Roman Catholicism in spite of the trials it caused him. Although he was not involved in ecumenical activities, as the term is commonly understood today, his whole life was ecumenical in outlook. If he had directed his attention to this movement, which has received such a great impetus since Vatican II and whose essential spirit consists of focusing attention on Christ-Omega rather than on the differences between various Christian churches, I am sure that he would have said that all elements of true value in the various Christian churches can and will be preserved as Christendom reunites.

The same applies to other religions, to various political systems, to the different races. Judaism for example should not look upon Fr. Teilhard's theory as being anti-Jewish because it is pro-Christian, for who can say with certainty that the second coming of Christ which Christians hope for and the Messianic Age which Jews have looked forward to and worked for for thousands of years are not but two different ways of thinking of the endpoint of evolution. Similarly, negroes, Chinese, Hindus or any other non-white, non-European-stock, non-Judaeo-Christian people should not view his vision as excluding them or being antithetical to their traditions, cultures and desires. In our bodies, cells are arranged in organs and they in turn constitute our bodies. Using our previous analogy of cells as persons let us now extend it and draw a parallel between organs and social groupings. Does this not help us see how there must be a diversity of *cooperating* social groupings for a higher being to be complete, to be fulfilled? Just as each person contributes something unique to society, so each grouping of persons serves God in some special way by virtue of its existence. Omega, the endpoint of converging evolution, is the ultimate of diversity in unity.

* * * * * *

> Remain true to yourselves, but move ever upwards to greater consciousness and greater love! At the summit you will find yourselves united with all those who, from every direction, have made the same ascent. For everything that rises must converge.[51]

We do have it in our power to change the world and make it a better place in which to live; *we can* help in building heaven for the simple reason that we are evolution become aware of itself; *we must* do this lest we perish.

A new way of seeing, combined with a new way of acting: that is what we need. If we have captured the vision we must apply it. What we have to do is make up our minds and get to work—*quickly, right now*. We must try to overcome our prejudices (often times openly admitted but frequently not) against anyone with whom we don't agree. Unless we learn that every time we interact with another person we're either building or destroying the earth (depending on our attitude) then we haven't grasped the fundamental condition for survival. Unless we learn to love—everywhere, at all times, under all circumstances—then we're not learning to work with the evolutionary tide.

As Fr. Teilhard said "It is of no use to read these pages, or other similar pages written twenty centuries ago, merely with one's eyes. Anyone who without having put his hand to the plough, thinks he has mastered them is deluding himself. *We must try to live them.*"[52]

Appendix I

Thermodynamics, The Two Energies and Life

As this book has shown the changes which occur with time in matter, in living organisms and in the society of man can be understood in terms of a law of complexity-consciousness proposed by Fr. Teilhard. Changes—any changes—in physical systems are caused by energy because energy is that which produces effects, or can produce effects. And so, viewing the cosmos as a vast physical system which is undergoing evolutionary changes, Fr. Teilhard reasoned that there must be 'an energy' producing these changes just as there must be 'an energy' which causes water to boil. To him it was inexplicable that the evolution of matter, of life and of society could be following the same pattern of change unless there was a reason for it.

For purposes of discussion he classified energy as being either tangential or radial. The former is 'ordinary' energy and the latter that which causes evolutionary changes. In actuality Fr. Teilhard did not affirm that there are two completely distinct and separate energies because all energy is just energy; instead he merely talked about two different kinds for convenience. But since the consequences of this more general approach to energy (in particular the consequences of the idea of radial energy) are troublesome to many persons this appendix has been prepared. Its purpose is to show that Fr. Teilhard's ideas, properly understood, are not antiscientific.

Energy is something which we know exists but which we only know about indirectly. That is to say, energy is not something which we ordinarily perceive directly through sense experience. If, instead of being *something*, energy were *some thing* then we could detect it directly with our five senses. But in general we can't do this. For example, if we touch a hot pan on the stove with our fingers we perceive that it is hot but we don't automatically know that some thermal energy has been transferred from the pan to our fingers. The idea of thermal energy having been transferred from the pan to our fingers is a concept or a mental picture of what happened. Although it is impossible to draw a sharp line of distinction between a perception of reality and a conception of reality and to say that anything and everything can be neatly categorized in one of these two ways to the exclusion of the other, it does not seem to be incorrect or unreasonable to say that energy is primarily a concept of reality rather than a percept of reality.

The 'fact' that energy is something can be shown by experiments. For example even though no one can show you a calorie they can demonstrate that the temperature of a hot and cold object approach one another with the passage of time or perform some other equivalent experiment. We deduce from such experiments that 'something' must have been transferred from the hot object to the cold object or, more generally, from one at a higher potential in some sort of a force field to one at a lower potential. This 'something' we call energy.

Energy as we normally think of it (viz.—tangential energy) is an immensely useful concept and there are no valid grounds for questioning the science of energy, thermodynamics, at least for macroscopic systems containing large numbers of elemental particles. It is a tribute to the power of collective human minds that we, mankind, were able to evolve the concept of energy and the structure and mathematical formalism of thermodynamics.

Nevertheless it is important to realize that energy is an abstraction, an idea, a word pertaining to certain aspects of the real world which can only be tested by experience if the concept has an operational meaning. Now a concept, any concept, has an operational meaning only if we can give an operational definition of the concept. That is, we can make sense of the concept only if we can specify a procedure by which to test its validity. If we can not conceive of a way to test a concept, if we can not in some way compare it with experience to see if it jibes with the facts as we know them then it is a meaningless concept.

In the case of tangential energy the operational definition whereby we give meaning to the concept consists of the specification of any one of a number of *experimental* procedures by which we can measure the amount of that which we call energy. Such experiments have been conducted an innumerable number of times. They invariably show that 'energy' is conserved. Therefore without hesitation we accept the concept of energy, tangential energy that is, as being a valid concept and we use the concept all the time without giving a second thought as to whether or not energy is real. The fact that we can and do use the concept is sufficient for us. However it should be remembered that this was not always the case; we humans didn't always have such a clear (!) understanding of (tangential) energy. It wasn't until the nineteenth century that the first definitive experiments were run and the word entered our vocabulary.

Today however we can say with assurance—if we accept the experimental evidence, which most of us do—that *the concept of tangential energy exists in our minds as an abstraction of experiments performed on matter* and that it is a concept without which we could not live as we do. Even more importantly, we can not live at all without the reality of which tangential energy is a concept. We need bread to survive. The 'fact' that it contains calories is secondary because humans survived on bread long before calories were invented by the mind of man.

Now let us consider Fr. Teilhard's concept of radial energy. As we shall see in the next few pages it is not defined, at the present time, through a set of *experimental* operations because we can not isolate and experiment with the whole universe and because, so far, no on has thought up another *experimental* way to check the validity of the concept. But this does not mean that his concept is invalid and therefore meaningless. It just means that another type of operational meaning must be employed.

In effect, the procedure by which Fr. Teilhard tested the validity of this concept was to observe nature, to deduce a fundamental 'law' of evolution, the law of increasing complexity-consciousness. One might say that he used the experiental rather than the experimental approach. From these observations of the evolutionary process he, as well as many others, finds the concept of radial energy to be a valid concept, even though it is not presently subject to experimental proof. (Who can say with certainty that it will never be?) Whether or not one accepts his arguments therefore depends on whether or not one 'sees' evolution in the same manner that he did.

If we do accept his arguments that everything we know of nature from our study of the physical, natural and social sciences fits into his 'law' of complexity-consciousness then we can say, also with assurance, that *the concept of radial energy exists in our minds as an abstraction of observations of nature.* Looked at this way the idea of radial energy gives us a more general understanding of the nature of energy because 'experiments performed on matter' are only a special and limited set of all possible 'observations of nature.' One might say, using the language of the mathematicians, that energy as we normally think of it is a sub-class or a special form of a more general type of energy.

Modern thermodynamics is concerned with energy interchanges between 'things' and with the transformation of energy from one form to another. In principle it can be applied to big things (e.g., the Milky Way) as well as little things (e.g., a speck of dust). They can be living or inert. Always, however, there must be *two* 'things' which are usually called the system, i.e., that 'thing' under study, and its environment. The environment is the rest of the universe. Because of this restriction thermodynamics cannot be applied to the whole universe. One of the basic tenants or foundation stones upon which the mathematical structure of thermodynamics is built is the acknowledged impossibility of reversing any natural process *in its entirety.*

Within this limitation thermodynamics is an extremely useful 'tool' for understanding nature. Its structure or mathematical formalism is strongly flavored by statistics and is built upon the foundation of the 'knowable.' Now as far as thermodynamics, as presently constituted, is concerned 'knowable' is synonymous with 'experimentally verifiable.' Thus a practitioner of thermodynamics, when engaged in his specialty, has to stick by the same rules upon which his science is based. He can justify using only experimentally verifiable facts when applying the theory to a particular thing or process.

Now let us consider the work of a theoretical thermodynamicist in contrast to the practitioner. If he's trying to extend the concepts of thermodynamics and insists on sticking with the same ground rules, viz.-'knowable' equals 'experimentally verifiable,' then he, obviously, has to abide by the rule he insisted upon. He may make very worthwhile contributions and many such scientists do, but his contributions, of necessity, will be of the same order; that is to say, they will be applicable only within the same 'dimensions' as present day thermodynamics. But suppose our theoretician is examining the ground rules or foundations of thermodynamics (much as Riemann did with Euclid's geometrical postulates) in the hopes of extending the range of applicability of thermodynamics. If he's a man who believes that the only way to know *anything* is by the experimental method then he's right back in the same boat with the first theoretician. However, if he's a man who recognizes that there are ways of knowing other than the current scientific way a whole new world opens up in front of him. How far he can go depends on his talents, insights and inspirations but I'm sure he is the type of thermodynamicist Fr. Teilhard would encourage were he still alive. I believe that someday someone will do this and add another dimension to our scientific thinking much the way Riemann's work a little over 100 years ago opened the door to the fourth dimension. In fact I think Fr. Teilhard has already 'opened the door' even though he wasn't a thermodynamicist.

Unfortunately however, I believe, many scientists seem to carry the scientific mode of thinking over to all their thinking and, accordingly, believe that experimental verification is the only way of knowing anything. But this is an assumption on their part and nothing but an assumption. They are basing their life on an unproven postulate and, like Euclidians in a pre-Riemannian age, have built up an elaborate picture of reality which, although not necessarily incorrect, is nevertheless incomplete. They are looking only at a 'projection' of reality onto the 'plane' of the tangible and are assuming that the projection in which they make measurements is all there is to reality. The scientist who says that the only way to know *anything* is to measure it, or its effects, by the scientific method is assuming, without the proof he ordinarily demands, that the scientific method is the sole means of gaining knowledge. He may think no one can know something via another means (whatever it might be—inspiration, Revelation, even extra sensory perception, or something else—is not the point here) but he can't prove that they can't by his scientific methods. He's putting his faith in the scientific method which (I presume) he thinks is an objective reality in itself. But it isn't, because, at its roots, it is built upon what people think and believe, how they act and what they write in the scientific journals. He's trusting in a science which cannot say anything about how the universe as a whole is behaving.

To help these people see that maybe Fr. Teilhard's ideas on the two energies aren't so strange or scientifically heretical after all I would ask them these questions. "When we think of energy aren't we ordinarily thinking of tangential energy?" "Aren't we conditioned to think that because tangential energy is the only kind we can measure (now), it's the only kind there is?" "Do we really have objective scientific proof that there couldn't be a radial energy such as that described by Fr. Teilhard?"

Scientists who say we know only by measuring things are following the rules of the game of science, as we presently understand them, and this is understandable. But haven't they forgotten that most creative accomplishments in science involve or represent breaking the rules, taking speculative leaps of imagination? Neils Bohr for example proposed the 'unreasonable' idea that an atom couldn't have any arbitrary energy but only certain discrete energies. His theory was a hybrid between some 'classical' ideas and other ideas which, at the time, were seemingly unrelated. Bohr's theory met with astonishing success by accounting for many previously unexplained experimental results. In time it too became modified as more was learned but the significant point is that Bohr's contribution was only made because he broke the rules of the game of his time. It seems to me that Fr. Teilhard's 'bold speculation' concerning radial energy falls in the same category as Bohr's contribution.

Due to the nature of energy it is really not proper to think of different kinds of energy. Mechanical energy isn't anything different from nuclear energy. Both of them are just energy. We speak of different 'kinds' of energy, but only for convenience. In fact science tells us that any 'kind' of energy can be converted, in principle, to any other 'kind.' We can not visualize exceptions to this because of the nature of energy. In the same way, Fr. Teilhard says that tangential and radial energies are but different forms of the same energy. In fact he says that *all* energy is psychic energy. Since present day thermodynamics does not say anything about the ultimate philosophical nature of energy or of reality (it uses only an *experimental* operational definition of that reality which is) Fr. Teilhard's statement that all energy is essentially psychic in nature is not incompatible with present day thermodynamics to my way of thinking. He has not violated thermodynamics, he has gone beyond it.

And so just as there can be an interconversion between different 'kinds' of tangential energy, Fr. Teilhard shows that tangential and radial energies can somehow be exchanged. The mechanism of exchange must be somewhat different than in the case of the tangential types however because tangential and radial energies are dependent on one another, and yet, at the same time, they're independent.

> First of all the dependence. This is depressingly and magnificiently obvious. 'To think, we must eat' . . . Yet, seductive though it may be, the idea of a *direct* transformation of one of the energies into another is no sooner glimpsed than it has to be abandoned. As soon as we try to couple them together, their mutual inpendendence comes as clear as their interrelation.—Once again: 'To think, we must eat.' But what a variety of thoughts we get out of one slice of bread.[53]

This paradoxical behavior led Fr. Teilhard to conclude that it would be impossible to find a mechanical equivalent of will or thought. As indicated previously he thought there is in our universe another dimension, essentially spiritual in nature, of which we are not yet sufficiently aware and which we will have to take into account before a 'scientific' one-to-one correlation can be made between tangential and radial energies. But, "in last analysis, *somehow or other*, there must be a single energy operating in the world. And the first idea that occurs to us is that the 'soul' must be as it were a focal point of transformation at which, from all points of nature, the forces of bodies converge, to become interiorized and sublimated in beauty and truth."[53]

An intriguing feature of Fr. Teilhard's concept of the two energies is a conclusion which follows from the postulate, namely that the energy of the universe is *not* constant as many physics and chemistry textbooks state. Rather it is continually increasing. At first sight this astonishing idea appears to be in direct contradiction to a hundred years of scientific observations. It violates the "law" of conservation of energy.

Without fail whenever a scientist or engineer performs a quantitative energy balance on any kind of a reaction which occurs in any kind of a macroscopic physical process he invariably finds that some energy has been 'lost' in the process. If he's careful he can usually account for all the energy transfers between a system and its environment and hence the "law" of conservation of energy. But a part of his accounting procedures, an item on his balance sheet is that amount of energy which has been 'lost.' Its amount is calculable from thermodynamics using the Carnot principle.

This loss is a consequence of the second law of thermodynamics, an exception to which has never been observed in macroscopic systems. The second law states that the entropy change of a reversible process is zero and that in any irreversible reaction the entropy always increases.

Entropy is another very useful thermodynamic concept. Like energy, it's not a 'thing;' also like energy, it measures something. Energy is (a measure of) the capacity to do work, to produce effects, while entropy is (a measure of) uncertainty or disorder. The second law therefore says, in effect, that the uncertainty or the amount of disorder in the universe always increases. Stated another way, the second law says that the universe is tending towards the most probable state. A simple example will illustrate the idea. Take an ordered deck of cards and throw it up in the air. The probability that the cards will land on the floor neatly stacked up exactly the way they originally were is infinitesimally small. Most of us would say it's impossible, but strictly speaking it isn't. The amount of disorder—the uncertainty as to the location of a particular card—the entropy has increased. Some of the tangential energy consumed in initially arranging the cards has been lost forever.

Every reaction ever observed in a macroscopic system is irreversible, in its entirety. For example, if we isolate a system from its environment, and don't permit any mass or energy transfers between the system and the environment, the system will, in time, reach the most probable state, which is the state of maximum entropy for the system. Or, if we cause a reaction in a finite system to reverse by adding energy to the system from the environment, the entropy of the system *and* the environment will always increase even though the entropy of the system might decrease. Phrased another way, the second law tells us it is impossible to build a perpetual motion machine. (Present day thermodynamics however can not say whether or not One exists!) Thus the second law, which is based only on experimentally verifiable evidence, says that the universe is running out of useable energy. In the past and even today some scientists predict, on the basis of the second law, that it's just a question of time before the whole universe is just one disorganized, haphazard, *lifeless* mass of something-or-other. Lord Kelvin called this state of affairs the heat death of the universe.

Fr. Teilhard vehemently denies these pessimistic predictions of the future—on the basis of evolution which he believed is a cosmic process in which and by which cosmic matter ascends towards ever higher forms of life.

Living beings, whether they be amoebae or men have always perplexed thinking man because it is so difficult to define or describe life and because the growth of living things is so extraordinarily complicated. Beings, when they are alive, take the substances of the world (food, oxygen, etc.) and arrange them into very highly ordered 'things'—seemingly in contradiction to the universal trend noted in physics in which greater disorder (higher entropy) is always observed. When an organism dies entropy takes over in a very straightforward fashion as our bodies return to dust, but then, of course, life is no longer present, in the organism.

Experiments have shown however that metabolism, the process by which living organisms grow, does not violate the second law of thermodynamics. In other words, living things, whatever their specific natures, have to work to grow. Fr. Teilhard was aware of this, and yet, noted, as many others have, that life exhibits some sort of anti-entropic character.

> In terms of physics and chemistry, the phenomena of life are essentially characterized (in precise contrast to those of matter) by an evolution towards the *least* probable. Improbabilities in the huge and unstable molecules accumulated by organic matter; improbabilities in the incredibly complicated structure of the smallest protozoan; improbabilities of a rapidly increasing order in the formation of the higher animals and

their development into various and progressive types throughout the geological ages; finally, the supreme improbabilities of the appearance, conservation and organization of thought on the earth. Man is supported by a giddy scaffolding of improbabilities, to which each new progress adds a new platform.

Faced with the huge and undeniable fact of the regular ascent of a part of the world towards states of increasing improbability, science has hitherto tried to close or turn away its eyes . . . Now might there not be another possible picture, arising automatically from the simplest words we can discover in which to express our experiences of the universe? If, in the universe, we find ourselves confronted with two important movements of elementary unities, one towards the more probable and one towards the less, why not try to find in this dual current two phenomena of the same general nature, importance and order: two aspects or two directions of a single, extremely general event?

Why, in fact, should not life be a counterpart or inverse of entropy?[54]

Fr. Teilhard extended this idea even further:

But there is another aspect of things to be considered. Life taken as a whole does not manifest itself to our experience only as an advance into—probability. It also appears in the light of our scientific investigations as a continuous ascent towards greater consciousness. Beneath the ups and downs of the countless waves of organic forms runs a constantly mounting tide towards greater freedom, inventiveness and thought. Can we possibly think of this tremendous event as merely a secondary effect of cosmic forces? Can we view it as only a subordinate feature of the universe? For metaphysics, there is hardly a

> possible hesitation. For physics the question is just being put.[55]

Still, one may argue, has it not just been pointed out that metabolism does not violate entropy? Even though Fr. Teilhard has very eloquently expressed a possible solution to this problem his proposal just doesn't seem to jibe with the facts of science?

The key to this paradox lies, I think, in realizing: one, that thermodynamics does not apply to individual elements; two, that it is impossible to truly isolate an individual living being from its environment (and keep it alive) in order to scientifically evaluate whether, in actual fact, the living being does or does not obey the second law; and three, that a being who is alive can not be completely 'handled' by thermodynamics because there is as yet no way to plug the important and governing characteristic called life into thermodynamic equations. The last point is especially important and Fr. Teilhard made special note of it.

> It could still be objected against the physical equivalence of life and entropy that life is itself fundamentally governed by entropy since it is built of elements that are subject to the general laws of energy. But are we quite sure that in its completely vitalized radius (weak though this radius is) animate matter still dissipates energy in order to act? Let us not forget that the laws of physics are only valid for large numbers. Now the specifically living action of a living being (individual or collective) is essentially an isolated action, the action of a single element.[56]

Action is the crucial word here, the *free* action of a living element. Although the free and oftentimes improbable actions of a living being are not the only traits or 'properties' which characterize life they certainly are important ones. They are also those which most elude scientific explanation because science is concerned only with probablistic predictions. Science can say what is most likely to happen under certain conditions but it can not say what will happen in individual cases. And, as it, science, concerns itself with 'things' high on the centrated-complexity-consciousness scale its probablitic predictions become less certain. Could not the reason for this be that as science moves from 'things' in which the within is relatively unimportant (i.e., physics) to those in which it is more important (i.e., psychology) it is neglecting the most important aspect of the higher 'things,' namely the within?

Regarding this question of life and entropy there are other new ideas of a scientific nature which are beginning to fall into place along the general lines suggested by Fr. Teilhard. Specifically I have in mind some of the notions of information theory and the thermodynamics of open systems—both of which have quite recently been born, in a historic sense, as new scientific disciplines. This is not the place to try to describe these theories in any detail but a key feature of each should be mentioned.

Due to the pioneering work of Claude Shannon shortly after World War II we are now beginning to learn how to measure 'information' quantitatively and to appreciate that 'information' is a basic parameter of our universe, just as mass and energy (or space and time) are. 'Information' is not measured by counting books or college degrees. We haven't advanced far enough yet to measure the amount of 'information' one receives when he gets a diploma. At our still rather rudimentary stage of evolution 'information' is measured simply in terms of yes or no decisions. Shannon's contribution is nevertheless a remarkable step forward. It is fair to say that our present communications and computer systems never would have evolved to their present stage of development without information theory.

An intriguing aspect of Shannon's work and that of his followers is that 'information,' which can be interpreted as a measure of knowledge, is like negative entropy. The more information a system (e.g., a man) has the less the uncertainty is. To use the card example again, if after throwing the cards on the floor, we have yes or no 'information,' that is—knowledge, pertaining to one or more cards (e.g., that one over there is the three of spades and the other one over there is not a queen) our uncertainty as to the total configuration of cards on the floor is reduced. Thus, since entropy is uncertainty, 'information' is negative entropy.

Let us turn now to the other relatively new development. The thermodynamics of open systems treats nonisolated systems in contrast to 'classical' thermodynamics which treats only closed systems. It is thus more applicable to living beings because, as we saw earlier, if we isolate a being from its environment—that is, make it a closed system—it will no longer be alive.

Without going into further details it can be said that when the notions of information theory and the thermodynamics of open systems are appropriately combined many of the previously mentioned paradoxes disappear. Many of the supposed violations of physical laws in living nature do not exist. In fact a strong case can be made to support the idea that *the entropy of a living organism can decrease by the import of information.* This is especially true if the living being is a highly developed organism (viz., a man rather than an amoeba).

We are still a long way from quantitatively defining life but it seems to me these new ideas are perfectly compatible with Fr. Teilhard's vision. They reinforce my belief that his theory is substantially correct. Information is a measure of knowledge, knowledge is a characteristic of biological life, self-knowledge is what distinguishes men from animals. Although an infinite barrier must be jumped is it too much of an extrapolation to say that the supreme form of knowledge, God Himself, is causing evolution to progress towards ever higher forms of life by the infusion of 'information' into His creation in the form of radial energy? That, I think, is what Fr. Teilhard would have said had he been aware of information theory and the thermodynamics of open systems.

> Entropy and life; backward and forward: two complimentary expressions of the arrow of time. For the purposes of human action, entropy (a mass-effect rather than a law of the unit) is without meaning. Life, on the other hand, if it is understood to be the growing interiorization of cosmic matter, offers to our freedom of choice a precise line of direction.[57]

* * * * * *

It should be noted that in none of the discussion given herein has it been argued that our concepts of energy, any kind of energy, cause energy. I would say instead that energy is a manifestation of a reality which exists independently of any ideas or concepts we may have about it. We *define* energy in an abstract manner but it *is* a manifestation of reality. Previously it was pointed out, without introducing the idea of God, that tangential energy is a concept without which we could not live as we do (modern science and technology are unthinkable without a well developed idea of tangential energy), and that we could not live at all without the reality of which tangential energy is a concept. Can not precisely the same reasoning be applied to radial energy because radial and tangential energies are one and the same energy? To my mind that reality which is—or, in other words—that reality which exists independently of our ideas about it, that reality of which tangential and radial energies are present day concepts, that reality without which we can not live at all can be none other than He who told Moses "I Am Who Am." It is the same God who sent his only begotten Son into the world.

We need bread to live. That is obvious because we die of starvation if we don't get it. But what is bread? — it is matter; it has mass which is interconvertible to energy as Albert Einstein and Hiroshima taught us. If energy is nothing but a manifestation of reality is not bread also but another manifestation of reality? Therefore does it not follow that the whole universe, material and spiritual, is a manifestation of that Reality which is, of the one God who has told us that He has created everything and that it is good?

We know that we need bread to live and the Gospels tell us that man does not live by bread alone. Is there any contradiction here? I think not. The meaning of Christ's teachings takes on a much deeper significance when the universe is viewed from Fr. Teilhard's perspective. Just as Albert Einstein showed us how mass and energy are unified, Fr. Teilhard has shown us how the material and spiritual are unified. They are all manifestations of the same thing, which isn't a thing but a Person. The triune God, three Persons with one Nature, is that reality which is.

Our concepts of this Reality may and do change with time, but God, of whom our concepts are merely verbal expressions, does not. In fact our concepts of God must change with time as we grow and mature—otherwise we won't be truly growing and maturing in the fullest (evolutionary) sense. Since we, as individuals and as a species, are all part of God's evolutionary process of change, unless we change our concepts of Him in such a way that our knowledge of Him is roughly comparable with our knowledge of His creation then He may very well die within us. Is not the lack of this necessary change in ones concept of God precisely the cause of many a modern man's disillusionment with God, and the source of most of the world's problems? It is no wonder that a modern man with a third grade or middle ages concept of God as a 'white-bearded-man-up-there-somewhere' does not find this adequate. Such a man may easily lose his faith or never find it because his knowledge of God has not kept pace with his knowledge of the world.

I will conclude this Appendix with the following food for thought. We have said that one of the philosophical foundations of thermodynamics is expressible by the sentence: "It is impossible to reverse any natural process in its entirety. Put into more formal language in the form of the second law of thermodynamics this notion tells us that the universe is tending towards its most probable state, yet we admit that thermodynamics cannot say anything about how the whole universe is behaving. The second law phrased this way, and interpreted in the light of Fr. Teilhard's vision, says to me that the universe is tending towards Omega because I think Omega *is* the universe's most probable final state. It is not a certain final state, however, because we people can thwart evolution by refusing to love God and our neighbor. Viewed this way I am impressed by the insights thermodynamics gives us. At the same time I think we must take care that we don't make science our God.

Dr. Edgar Taschdjian, in a review of *The Vision of the Past* aptly expressed this idea in a different manner. He pointed out that Shannon's theory of communications has made it clear that even communications of thoughts by means of symbolic messages (written texts or oral communications) are as subject to the laws of entropy as any other physical process. Because of random perturbations or 'noise' in communications channels a message sent is received only with a certain degree of probability, not with absolute certainty. Applying this to the transmission and reception of God's word and recognizing that man is a free creature who often hears the message without listening to it, Dr. Taschdjian says, "even divine grace cannot work its wonders unless the human receiver is willing to listen; the seeds of the divine word fall mostly on the rocks and under the thorns and only a few will germinate and bear fruit. This, in biblical language, is entropy . . . the original sin from which the whole world suffers."

Appendix II

Sin, Suffering and Hell

In the preface to his book *Teilhard de Chardin, The Man and His Meaning* Fr. Henri de Lubac concisely voiced what seems to be the most sensible way to view Fr. Teilhard's vision.

> If Pere Teilhard's 'vision' is integrated in the great Christian experience, it is also clear that it expresses only one aspect of it. Similarly, the road he followed with such determination is, and cannot but be, only one of the converging roads that lead to Christ: The road, maybe, that best answers the expectations of our days, but that must fail to reach its destination if it claims to be the only road. Pere Teilhard, following up the graces given to him, explored deeply a part, but only a part, of the domain in which are to be found "the unfathomable riches of Christ."[58]

Neither Fr. de Lubac nor Fr. Teilhard ever said that Fr. Teilhard's 'scientific, unified-vision way to Christ' was the only way so there is no argument on this point. The fact is that it is a very appealing way to many persons for a variety of reasons—not the least of which is that it emphasizes the positive rather than the negative. Love, the value of human effort, creation, progress are all included in a positive manner, which is most inspiring to those who can see the way he did.

Yet we know that suffering, evil and sin are a

part of life and of the world, and divine Revelation teaches us there is also a hell. These negative aspects of reality do not appear, at first sight, to be compatible with Fr. Teilhard's vision. And so an apparent inconsistency or defect in his 'theory' arises because he claimed that his vision encompassed everything.

The purpose of these few pages is to sketch, very briefly, the general lines illustrating how they too can be understood in terms of Fr. Teilhard's vision. The reader should realize however that Fr. Teilhard did not claim to have completely explained or justified suffering and misery, to have fully understood sin or to have entirely and rigorously catagorized hell in the scheme of things. Therefore his treatment of these negative aspects of reality, like those of all other writers who have addressed themselves to these topics, should only be considered as a partial 'explanation.' In actual fact his writings on these subjects are very meager in terms of number of pages. They are found principally in *The Divine Milieu*, a book which is essential to a complete understanding of his ideas.

In order to relate sin and suffering to Fr. Teilhard's vision the most important point to note is that his view of the world as it exists is that of *a world in the process of being perfected*. It is not yet perfect; ergo, it is imperfect. Sin and suffering are manifestations of this imperfection. To many people, this may seem to be an inadequate 'explanation,' but that, in a nutshell, is what he said.

We can look at the situation in a slightly different way by considering Fr. Teilhard's thoughts on entropy and life as discussed in Appendix I. If we accept his ideas that life, which is 'directed' by God's love, and entropy are two opposing and fundamental tendencies in the cosmological process—the one leading to eternal life with God and the other to complete and total death—then I think it is not improper to think of sin as moral entropy. Which amounts to saying that sin is any non-Christ-centered (free) action of the individual person.

Suffering is another kind of manifestation of entropy, or of the negative aspect of reality. However it differs from sin in that its effects (i.e., physical deterioration) can be turned around, so to speak, by the will of the individual who is suffering. Suffering then can represent one of the highest means for reaching eternal life.

Though at times he became very discouraged, Fr. Teilhard was by nature an optimist. His personality was such that he was able to see the positive side of things. For example he was able to see how wars served their purpose in the evolutionary scheme of things. They inevitably bring people together, cause them to converge! He never advocated war as a means for causing persons to converge but just recognized, since convergence is about all that wars do accomplish, that that must be how they are a part of God's plan.

This is not to say that God causes wars directly. It's just that He built His universe in such a way that there are two opposing tendencies in it. God wanted man, whom He created in His image, to have a choice, just as He does. God has the choice to create or not to create. And so do we. We can choose to build the earth for Him, or not to. The latter choice amounts to working against Him because of the way the world is.

He chose (and chooses—the tense is immaterial since God transcends time) to create and sustains creation by His creating action. Since we are a part of His continuing creation and would not even exist if it weren't for Him we just have to live according to His plan. In this we have no choice. But we do have a choice, since we exist, to work 'for' or 'against' evolution. If we choose the 'entropy way' and work against the evolutionary tide—anarchy, disorder, hatred, selfishness, greediness, etc.—then we frequently end up fighting one another in wars and cause all kinds of lesser miseries. So we conclude that wars are caused by man yet they nevertheless fit into God's plan.

The tragedy is that there need not be war. If only man would recognize the structure of the universe and see that God is the beginning and the end, the source of his life and his goal would he not then freely choose to work with the evolutionary tide rather than against it? Would not then war, suffering, poverty, misery and ignorance be reduced at an ever accelerating rate as man reawakens his hope and faith in the future and works for the end of the world, the Parousia of Christ?

And why don't we all freely accept our ultimate goal? It's because of the sin of pride. We substitute man for God and believe that we can build the world by ourselves without His help. I think we must learn to swallow our pride, humbly admit to God that we've erred, that we can't live without Him, and then proceed to right our wrongs and build the earth for Him so that God may be all in all.

These few remarks by an amateur lay theologian, which are perhaps wide of their mark, are intended to introduce the following thought which several more competent commentators have pointed out. . . . Fr. Teilhard's vision emphasizes *Creation* and *Incarnation,* whereas most other Christian writers emphasize *Sin* and *Redemption.* I don't think these two 'ways to Christ' are incompatible. Instead, as Fr. de Lubac implied, they are but two of the converging roads which lead to the same Christ.

I can think of no better way to end this book than by a prayer. It is from *The Divine Milieu* and is relevant to the problem of sin and hell.

> Your revelation, O Lord, compels me to believe more . . . there is not only *nether* darkness; there is also *outer* darkness. That is what the Gospels tell us.
>
> Of the mysteries which we have to believe, O Lord, there is none, without a doubt, which so affronts our human views as that of damnation. And the more human we become . . . the more lost we feel at the thought of hell. We would perhaps understand falling back into inexistence —but what are we to make of eternal uselessness and eternal suffering?
>
> You have told me, O God, to believe in hell. But you have forbidden me to hold with absolute certainty that a single man has been damned. I shall therefore make no attempt to consider the damned here, nor even to discover—by whatsoever means—whether there are any. I shall accept the existence of hell on Your word, *as a structural element in the universe,* and I shall pray and meditate until that awe-inspiring thing appears to me as a strengthening and even blessed complement to the vision of Your omnipresence which You have opened out to me . . .
>
> The existence of hell, then, does not destroy anything and does not spoil anything in the divine milieu whose progress all around me I have followed with delight . . . It adds an accent, a gravity, a contrast, a depth which would not exist without it. The peak can only be measured from the abyss which it crowns.[59]

GLOSSARY

Biogenesis—biological evolution; the evolutionary process by which living organisms change from one species to another over extended periods of time.

Biosphere—that relatively thin region near the surface of our earth in which all living things and beings exist. It consists of the seas, the lower atmosphere and the outermost crust of the earth itself. Sometimes the term is applied to the aggregate of all living things rather than to the medium in which they live.

Christogenesis—the final phase of evolution as envisioned by Fr. Teilhard. Historically it began with the birth of Christ but it is only gradually supplanting the prior evolutionary process of noogenesis as time marches on. Its primary characteristic is an attitude of genuine love among all men regardless of race, color, creed or nationality. Expression of this attitude in the form of action unifies mankind and draws men nearer to God, their creator.

Complexity—a characteristic of structures of all kinds whether they be planets, living organisms, machines or social institutions. As used by Fr. Teilhard the term is a measure of the number of simpler elements comprising a more complex 'thing' *and* of the number, type and quality of bonds, links and associations among the elements.

Complexity-consciousness, law of—an evolutionary law expounded by Fr. Teilhard which states that complexity tends to increase with the passage of time. At the present stage of evolution, the cosmos has evolved to the point where a portion of cosmic matter has become so complex that it has acquired the property of consciousness. The most significant portion, man, has even become self-conscious. The law of centrated-complexity-consciousness expresses the thought that evolutionary progress is understandable by the sequence: energy-matter-life-reflective thought-spirit. Evolutionary progress, and therefore all progress, is thus measured in terms of the scale of complexity-consciousness whose terminal point in the future is the Omega point.

Cosmogenesis—The first phase of evolution in which matter was formed from energy and assumed ever more complex forms as time passed on. Fr. Teilhard believed that the Omega point of evolution was also the Alpha point and that the Alpha point, which is God, is the source of the energy from which the cosmos was and is being created.

Energy—that which can produce effects; the capacity to do mechanical, electrical or many other kinds of 'work.' Energy is interconvertible with mass or matter according to the famous equation $E = mc^2$. Technically speaking it is a concept of the world all about us which can only be given a precise meaning in terms of some sort of operational definition. See also radial energy and tangential energy.

Entropy—uncertainty; disorder. Entropy, like energy, is another concept of the world all about us which can only be given a precise meaning in terms of some sort of operational definition. Entropy is a measure of time because scientific observation shows that entropy invariably increases with the passage of time. Fr. Teilhard asserts that there is another measure of time, namely life, and that the two—entropy and life—are measures of time in an opposing sense. Time probably only runs one way and we can measure its passage in terms of degradation (entropy) or in terms of elevation (to 'higher' forms of life).

Hominisation—the progressive psychosocial evolution of man; the process whereby mankind's potentialities are more and more fully realized in the world, and all the forces contained in the inert and animal worlds are progressively spiritualized in human civilization; the maturing of individual man and of mankind in the fullest evolutionary sense.

Information—a measure of knowledge; negative entropy. The 'information' content of a 'thing' is intimately related to its complexity and consciousness in a manner which we are just beginning to understand. 'Information' is a basic parameter or concept of our universe which is proving to be extremely useful in understanding nature. Like energy and entropy it can only be given a precise meaning in terms of some sort of operational definition.

Lithosphere—the outer crust of the earth.

Noogenesis—that phase of evolution which began when man appeared some one and a half million years ago. It is distinguished from biogenesis in that noogenesis is evolution in the domain of reflective life. Thus, rather than being manifested by the progressive formation of ever more complex biological organisms it is manifested by the growth of ever more complex and interrelated social institutions which are raising man's awareness of his place in nature.

Noosphere—that 'envelope' surrounding the earth which is made up of the thoughts of all men; the totality of ideas, philosophies and knowledge which mankind has stored in its (collective) mind. It is growing every day.

Nucleon—a subatomic elementary particle such as an electron, proton or neutron. Since the advent of the atomic age, scientists are learning that these particles in turn are composed of even more elementary 'particles' such as mesons, muons, etc.

Omega, Omega point—the end point of evolution; God. Omega is also Alpha. God is the beginning and the end, just as alpha and omega are the first and last letters of the Greek alphabet.

Psychic Temperature—a figure of speech which expresses the thought that there is a 'temperature,' analogous to thermal temperature, which measures the intensity or the degree of withinness in a clump of matter, or an organism, or a being, or a social institution, or in the whole world.

Radial energy—that form of energy which is responsible for the evolution of the cosmos towards ever more complex, more aware, more spiritual 'things.' Radial energy reveals itself to man from a study of evolution. Since it is also a manifestation of God's love we also know something about it, though not by the name of radial energy, from divine Revelation.

Social institutions—any collection of persons organized formally or informally for a purpose. Examples are families, governments, races, corporations, religious bodies, etc.

Tangential energy—that form of energy which is associated with the tangible reality of the cosmos. Calories are a common measure of tangential energy. The amount of tangential energy which a body gives up or receives when it changes its state or form can be measured by means of a variety of scientific instruments. Tangential energy is always measured *relative* to some arbitrary standard. Thus we can never assign an absolute value to it.

Verticil—a series of 'things,' each of which evolved from its predecessor in a direct fashion. In a more restricted sense it is a whorl or circle, as of leaves, hairs, etc., arranged round a point on an axis.

Within—the inner, intangible aspect of all things, beings and institutions.

Without—that aspect of all things, beings and institutions which is detectable by sense experience.

LIST OF QUOTATIONS CITED

Reference No.

i	*Building the Earth,* p. 54
ii	*Letters from a Traveler,* p. 224–225
iii	*The Future of Man,* p. 52
1	*Hymn of the Universe,* p. 99–100
2	Claude Cuenot, *Pierre Teilhard de Chardin,* translated by Vincent Colimore (Helicon Press, Baltimore, 1965), p. 21
3	*The Making of a Mind,* p. 241
4	*Hymn of the Universe,* p. 153–154

5 *The Divine Milieu*, p. 11
6 *The Future of Man*, p. 309
7 *The Phenomenon of Man*, p. 55
8 *Man's Place in Nature*, p. 20
9 *The Future of Man*, p. 109
10 *Man's Place in Nature*, p. 24
11 *The Phenomenon of Man*, p. 121
12 *The Phenomenon of Man*, p. 77–78
13 *Vision of the Past*, p. 72–73
14 *Man's Place in Nature*, p. 63
15 *The Phenomenon of Man*, p. 160
16 *The Phenomenon of Man*, p. 186
17 *The Phenomenon of Man*, p. 188
18 *The Vision of the Past*, p. 157
19 *The Phenomenon of Man*, p. 65
20 *The Phenomenon of Man*, p. 164–165
21 *The Future of Man*, p. 113

Reference No.

22 *Man's Place in Nature*, p. 108
23 *The Future of Man*, p. 133
24 *The Future of Man*, p. 113-114
25 *Vision of the Past*, p. 252
26 *Man's Place in Nature*, p. 99-100
27 *Man's Place in Nature*, p. 81
28 *The Future of Man*, p. 228
29 *The Future of Man*, p. 115
30 *Teilhard de Chardin Album*, p. 37
31 *Building the Earth*, p. 83
32 *The Vision of the past*, p. 230-231
33 *The Future of Man*, p. 207
34 *The Future of Man*, p. 287
35 Christopher Mooney, *Teilhard de Chardin and the Mystery of Christ*, p. 142-143
36 *The Phenomenon of Man*, p. 271
37 *The Future of Man*, p. 207 and p. 287

38 *The Future of Man*, p. 116-117
39 *The Divine Milieu*, p. 119-120
40 *Teilhard de Chardin Album*, p. 138
41 *The Phenomenon of Man*, p. 31
42 Colossians 1:16-17
43 *Teilhard de Chardin Album*, p. 191
44 *The Future of Man*, p. 75-76
45 *Teilhard de Chardin Album*, p. 101
46 *Hymn of the Universe*, p. 118

LIST OF QUOTATIONS CITED

Reference No.

47 *Hymn of the Universe*, p. 149 and *Divine Milieu*, p. 137
48 *Building the Earth*, p. 56
49 *The Appearance of Man*, p. 239
50 *The Vision of the Past*, p. 213-214
51 Attributed to Teilhard, original source unknown.
52 *Hymn of the Universe*, p. 131
53 *The Phenomenon of Man*, p. 63-64
54 *The Vision of the Past*, p. 168-169
55 *The Vision of the Past*, p. 150
56 *The Vision of the past*, p. 169-170 in a footnote
57 *The Future of Man*, p. 48-49
58 Henri de Lubac, *Teilhard de Chardin, The Man and His Meaning*, p. v-vi
59 *The Divine Milieu*, p. 129-130